# That'd be Right

A fairly true history of modern Australia

# William McInnes

hachette
AUSTRALIA

hachette
AUSTRALIA

Published in Australia and New Zealand in 2008
by Hachette Australia
(An imprint of Hachette Australia Pty Limited)
Level 17, 207 Kent Street, Sydney NSW 2000
www.hachette.com.au

This edition published in 2009

National Library of Australia
Cataloguing-in-Publication data

McInnes, William
That'd be right / William McInnes.

2nd ed.

ISBN 978 0 7336 2432 2 (pbk.)

McInnes, William.
Actors - Australia - Biography.
Fathers and sons - Australia - Biography.
Sports stories - Anecdotes.
Australia - History - Anecdotes.

792.028092

Set in Adobe Garamond by Bookhouse, Sydney
Cover design: Christabella Designs
Cover image © Getty Images
Author photograph: Lorrie Graham
Inside cover photograph: Sarah Watt
Printed in Australia by Griffin Press, Adelaide

Hachette Australia's policy is to use papers
that are natural, renewable and recyclable products
and made from wood grown in sustainable forests.
The logging and manufacturing processes are
expected to conform to the environmental
regulations of the country of origin.

For Stella

# 1

Open Sesame and I watched the big car slowly roll along the road towards where we stood. Not many people had a Mercedes Benz in the 1970s. They were big cars and you could see them for miles away, cruising around the streets like ships. I stood outside my home and waited as the car came rolling down the hill and through the new lights at Crash Corner. Across the road, at the top of Ella Street, stood Open Sesame. He waited like he always did, and watched. He lived down towards the beach in a small chamfer-board house and would walk up to the busy road to stand. And wait.

The car sailed past the brown brick house with the wooden carvings from Papua New Guinea and past the house with the bore water pump in its front yard.

My father said Open Sesame liked to play spotto and my mother said he was a little touched – harmless but not quite right.

'He's nearly there but not quite right. That's all.'

We never knew his name, but my father christened him Open Sesame one day.

Open Sesame had been standing in his slippers and his long cotton drawstring jammies watching the traffic, flicking his head from car to car.

'Poor bugger, that's not up to speed,' my father said as he wandered in from parking his truck.

Occasionally Open Sesame would crouch to get a better look at a car roaring past, which gave anybody watching him a good look at his wherewithal as his pyjamas' fly gaped open.

'Open Sesame!' my father yelled as the traffic watcher crouched and gaped. 'Show us your goodies!'

'There's a nice sight before breakfast,' said my mother.

My old man wandered off across the road and had a chat to the newly christened Mr Sesame. He patted him on the back and Open Sesame disappeared down Ella Street armed with a new name.

I looked across the road at Open Sesame as the Mercedes Benz drew closer. He looked like everyone else, save for a perpetually worried look on his face. It was as if he gazed at the day, but was contemplating something far greater, far more mysterious.

One morning Dad and I nodded a greeting to Open Sesame as we walked down to the beach. 'He always looks like he's trying to think about something important... Something big. Like he's thinking about life,' I said.

My father looked down at me. 'Him? That fella...Open Sesame? Don't be bloody thick, he's just after a Kingswood. And good luck to him.'

Open Sesame wore his perplexed and troubled look as the big white Mercedes Benz started to slow.

'Hitler's car! Hitler's car!' he cried out.

The door opened and I hopped into the deep red, leather back seat next to my friend David West. In the front were his parents. My parents were too busy to take me to the baseball that weekend, so the Wests were picking me up.

I settled into the back seat and said good morning to Mr and Mrs West. To me they seemed incredibly old and unbelievably polite.

Mr West looked down the lane that led to our house. He pursed his lips and took in the image of Gough Whitlam smiling down from the placard that was hammered into the entrance of our drive. It was the morning of election day 1975. That's why my parents were busy – they were off working on one of the voting booths, handing out how-to-vote cards for the Labor candidate.

'I see your father's tacked his colours out again this year,' said Mr West.

I didn't really understand what he meant so I just smiled.

He didn't say it nastily or with any edge, he was a nice man. The Wests had a shop in the arcade in Redcliffe that had different coloured roofs. It was the closest that the Redcliffe Peninsula came to a delicatessen. The shop was sparsely decorated with such delicacies as pork pies. The Wests were English. And more than that, Mr West informed me in his soft English accent, 'Well, I'm a small businessman. So there we are.' A soft whistle floated from the front seat when he said his s's.

I smiled a bit more for I had no idea why he was telling me this.

'You've got a shop,' I said. And, thinking I should make it sound grander, I added, 'And it's in the arcade...' I tried to think of anything else to do with the shop... 'Mum says your pie things are dear...but good.'

'Well, quality sometimes has a price,' said David.

Mr West didn't say anything.

Mrs West turned her white-haired head and smiled at me. I smiled. She smiled. David smiled. Gough smiled. Everyone was smiling, except Mr West who kept softly whistling.

'What is your friend trying to say?' Mrs West said.

I smiled back.

'Your friend,' she said again, pointing towards Open Sesame who was mouthing at us as we sat in the car.

'Mr Sesame?'

Mrs West smiled politely.

'He... He's just saying something... I think he likes your car.'

We drove off into the Saturday morning and I looked at Open Sesame and he stared after us with that look on his face. Trying to think, trying to make sense of something. Across the road Gough Whitlam, with his faintly supercilious eyebrows and his half smile, was almost mocking Open Sesame's efforts to make sense of the big question that haunted his thoughts.

Open Sesame stood still and I could see him open his mouth to speak. What he said I didn't know, but he waved and then stood stock still and leant back against the fence. I had no idea what it was he was trying to say and I didn't really pay much attention.

The Mercedes Benz purred along the road, David West and I chatted about the test match being played in Perth between Australia and the West Indies. Australia had been saved by former captain Ian Chappell from a complete thumping by the West Indies' pace attack. Chappell had scored 156 runs on the fastest wicket in the world and had pulled and hooked like a buccaneer.

Mr West whistled that he much preferred Ian's brother Greg who had taken over the captaincy.

'He's much more of a gentleman.' And then for good measure he added a thoughtful whistle, 'Ian's crude.'

'He can play though,' said David.

I thought of how Ian Chappell would constantly clutch and adjust his protector. My mother would make a face when she saw Chappell grip and pull. 'Why doesn't he wash himself, that man?'

'You what?' said my father.

'Always picking and poking.'

'Oh, come on, love, he's not playing with himself, he's having a think. There's a difference. You've got to know the game to see it.'

'Oh that'd be right... that's what you call it – having a think! Yes, you'd know, wouldn't you, Col.'

My father stared ahead, half closed his eyes and shook his head slowly.

I scratched myself and Ian Chappell continued to think.

In the car I looked back at Open Sesame. He looked back at me. He suddenly gripped at himself in a manner that Ian Chappell would have surely approved. He was deep in thought.

I took it as a sign to pass on my father's insights into the subtle intricacies of the game of cricket.

'He doesn't need a wash and he's not that itchy. He's not playing with himself. He's just thinking. Just...just thought you might want to know.'

David giggled. Mrs West still smiled, a little bit more tightly, and Mr West whistled patiently.

'Is he now?... Well, thank you very much.'

Open Sesame faded from my view and my memory. But not Gough Whitlam. He popped up here and there with that half-mocking smile as if the comings and goings of the day were a joke that only he could appreciate. It was almost as if he looked at me and said it was a lark, and I had a feeling that Gough was having a silent laugh at my expense.

Especially when I compared him to the great square-jawed glower of Malcolm Fraser who frowned down from telephone poles and trees. Where Gough Whitlam was all chubby-cheeked fun, Mal Fraser was very serious about everything. Fraser's picture was always sitting above the candidate for whatever electorate we drove through. It was slightly unnerving because the photos of the candidates were all very smiley and happy to be up there on the tree or shop window, or plonked in front yards and driveways.

They all looked like bad hairdressing cards: great mutton-chop sideburns, black horn-rimmed glasses, massive walrus moustaches, and great Brylcreemed sweeps of hair. It was like they were all dressed in some bad party disguises. And all of them it seemed were men. A boys' party.

Gough thinking it was fun and Mal grim-lipped in disappointment at the frivolity on such an important day.

It is hard to accept now that Fraser was only forty-five years old when he contested that election. Forty-five and a model image of the puritan conservative. Forty-five while Gough must have been close to sixty. Now Fraser is most people's favourite conservative prime minister. The old liberal conservative. And Gough still just seems to be Gough.

The cricket wasn't on until later in the day because of daylight saving so the radio was full of election news. The government, which was the caretaker one headed by square-jawed Mal, was expected to romp it in against the government that had been headed by smirking Gough until he'd been sacked by the Governor-General Sir John Kerr, a silly man who drank too much.

'I hope Whitlam wins,' I said, in the manner of wishing a football team would win a match.

'I hope he doesn't,' said David. 'I hate him...don't I?'

Mr West whistled politely. 'Yes, he's a communist and he's ruined this country, or done his very best to...but...' Mr West gave a lovely smile. 'Let's not mix politics and sport, never does any good.'

You're a small businessman, I thought. You sell odd food in an arcade with a coloured, see-through roof. Sometimes you pay for quality. You think Ian Chappell is crude. And you hate Gough Whitlam...

I may have been slow but I tried to read between the lines. I told myself not to mention the election again. And even to be careful about what I had to say about the cricket.

Still, he was a nice man and it was a lovely day.

And as the various Goughs and Mals whizzed by, with their hairy and odd-faced underlings beneath them, they began to look more and more like the portraits of the Tracy boys from the television series *The Thunderbirds*.

When I watched *The Thunderbirds* it was already a decade old, but it still seemed to air every day after school. It was an adventure series about an ex-astronaut billionaire with five sons who flew around the world saving people from disaster. There was a space station that eavesdropped on every bit of radio communication in the world to cherry pick which adventures the boys should pursue. The characters were puppets with huge heads and wobbly arms and they always wore weird clothes, like the ones migrants would buy from the St Vincent de Paul Society op shop down the road – skivvies, stripy polo jackets and trousers that were too short.

In fact they looked a lot like the men in the photos my sister would bring home from her work at a film-processing plant. For some reason men liked to take posed photos of themselves for dating agencies or matchmaking services, or maybe they just liked to pose in weird, Thunderbird clothes.

One sad little fellow had a series of self-portraits taken in various guises: with a tennis racquet, wearing a raincoat, in a dinner jacket, in a huge anorak with a furry hood like an Eskimo, in his underpants and then one I wasn't allowed to see but which would bring howls of laughter from the rest of my family. All the photos were taken in the same setting. His yard presumably, with a fern, a gnome and a concrete windmill, and he always wore the same vacant, glazed expression.

These men must have known that the photos would never be handed back to them and yet, I wonder if they ever complained? Or did they think it was enough that someone would see them, even with the knowledge that it might bring howls of laughter?

No wonder they looked so waxen and distant in the photographs.

I thought that Mal Fraser had the sort of expression that could have suitably been developed in between the holiday snaps and tour pictures.

Oddly enough, Mal came to end up with his trousers around his ankles in Memphis, courtesy of some South African Secret Police. And this was meant to humanise him.

I supposed if any of the Thunderbirds had sent photos of themselves in various states of undress into the photographic lab where my sister worked, they really wouldn't have had much to show, so it was no wonder their faces looked on in earnest, waxen blandness.

In the television show, whenever there was about to be some heroic action, Jeff Tracy, the patriarch puppet with the biggest and wobbliest head, would sit behind his desk, which looked like the bar at the Mariner's tavern, and would throw a switch and have a chat with one of his sons via a portrait in his office. The portraits' eyes would blink with a disconcerting brightness and the portraits would talk. I imagined the election posters mimicking the talking Tracy boys' portraits which signalled impending heroic action.

It made the car trip quite fun. Especially when I thought of Gough and Mal posing by the fern, the gnome and the windmill. Especially with the look on Gough's face.

The Wests had stopped chatting and the Mercedes Benz drifted to the ground where we were to play baseball.

I thought of what Mr West had said about politics and sport not mixing. It seemed to me that men like the candidates whose faces flashed past had little in common with men like Ian Chappell. Yes, some of them were hairy like Chappelli and perhaps some of them liked to think a lot like him, but I couldn't see much chance of them mixing.

My father was perplexed when it came to Whitlam.

'He's such a…a…smartarse. But he's got brains and, by Christ, he's got guts. You only have to look at Lang Park for that.'

Gough Whitlam once accepted an invitation from the Labor senator Ron McAuliffe to toss the coin and greet the players at a Rugby League match at Lang Park.

My father had always used this afternoon to illustrate the worth of Gough Whitlam, even though much of what Whitlam seemed to stand for was about as clear to 'the fellow at the bus stop as a roast pig saying the Lord's Prayer'.

It was the perceived sophistication of Whitlam – his embracing of the arts, his idolatry of the ancient civilisations and cultures – that jarred with my father.

'He nips off overseas and tells everybody over there what they don't know about their own history. It's all right to know more than the rest of us, but he seems to get a kick out of proving it.'

Gough Whitlam, Grecian scholar and lover of the arts, fronting Lang Park for a game of Rugby League. My father and his kind must have shaken their heads. The crowd let him have it.

They booed. They howled. The roar of disapproval was deafening. Whitlam slowly walked off with McAuliffe. He was a tall man, Whitlam, but he walked with a thigh-chafing gait.

'Never kicked a football in his life,' said my father.

But as he chafed his way from the field, Whitlam held himself taller than ever and turned to Senator Ron McAuliffe with a wink. 'Ron, I didn't realise you were so unpopular here.'

This story floated down through the Labor Party network. And my father nodded with approval.

'He's a brave bugger, you got to say that. Like an aristo in the tumbrels heading off to the guillotine. Good on him.'

It seemed that a crowd at a sporting event considered to be the 'working class' game had sensed that Whitlam didn't really belong. No politician is ever really given a resounding reception at big sporting events, especially the football. It's as if the crowd can collectively display that anti-authoritarian streak that Australians like to think they have. Especially men at an outdoor sporting event – a couple of beers, a few hours away from their lives and they dive full-length into the uncomplicated idea of being a man. It wasn't so much learnt behaviour back then, it wasn't encouraged, it was expected as a measure of a Sunday arvo in the sun.

But it was more than just a few boos to a bloke in a suit. It was like a baying call for Whitlam's head. My father nodded at the television screen, 'He's not long for the world that fella.'

On that fine Saturday on the 13th of December things seemed to unfold in a set and unhurried pattern. The Wests set up their camp chairs and flasks of tea and sandwiches and gently unfurled the great bedsheet of a newspaper that was *The Courier-Mail*, while we began to play baseball.

We played baseball to accompany our cricket, that's what the great Chappelli had done. So if it was good enough for that great thinker, it was good enough for us. It was an odd game though, all the backslapping, calling out and cheering seemed a bit embarrassing. A bit too demonstrative. 'A bit too American,' said Mrs West. 'But it's quicker than cricket.'

We were playing against the All Stars club and they all wore neat, ironed baseball outfits. We wore T-shirts and Stubbies.

Our club was filled with some incredibly large and hairy people, some of whom would occasionally give us juniors a glimpse of their social life.

One of the senior players, a rolling man with long dark hair, drove to the ground in a purple, hard-top Cortina, sat on a bench, unfolded a Bex paper, funnelled it into his mouth and washed it down for good measure with a can of Coke.

He began to unwrap a pie and said to nobody in particular, 'Had a seance last night in the graveyard.' He took a mouthful of his pie. A few heads turned to him.

'Oh yes?' said a man with no irony or colour in his voice.

'Yes,' said the pie-eater. 'Table was wonky and Carol fell over and cut herself. She cracked the shits and went home with her mum.'

'That's no good.'

'To be expected.'

'What'd you do?'

'Sank me six pack and went home.'

'That'd be right,' said the man, adjusting his cap.

The pie-eater gave a slight nod. And then belched.

I wondered if he had voted and who he had voted for. I wondered if he was a small businessman. I didn't think so, I couldn't imagine him in the delicatessen in the arcade with the coloured roof.

I looked back at the small business person I did know. I couldn't imagine him at a seance in the Redcliffe cemetery. The headline of *The Courier-Mail* he read proclaimed, 'Massive Swing To Libs'. He turned the page past the smirking Gough.

You're not long for this world.

Gough was in an advert with Kim Beazley Senior urging all Catholic parents to vote for Labor. I had heard my father laughing at this earlier in the morning.

'We're in trouble all right, off begging again.'

It was a memorable *Courier-Mail* edition. There was an ad for Condon Byrne from the DLP that a vote for him would 'Bring sanity back to the Senate'.

'Jesus Christ all bloody mighty,' my father said, 'that's like voting for a baboon with a hairy arse... it just doesn't happen. That bugger is as mad as a two-bob watch.'

There were lots of electoral slogans draped across the paper, between ads for McDonnell & East department store. Imported cork platform shoes duelled with the major parties' platforms – 'Maintain Your Rage' for the Labor Party and 'Turn on the Lights' for the Libs.

'Turn on the Lights' came complete with a song, sung by Renee Geyer.

'If I hear that woman with the big jaw howl that awful tune again,' growled my mum, 'I'll throw up.'

'I don't know why they want to turn the lights on, those buggers get more done in the dark,' she added.

The paper also contained a glorious story about two Playmates from the *Playboy* magazine in Sydney at the opening of a nightclub. One of them was called Bonnie Large. The story had accompanying photographs and detailed just how much money the Playmates had received and the fact that the winner of the Playmate of the Year had won a free car.

The pie-eater had also seen the story.

'Good bloody car, better than the Datsuns they give the footy players.'

I looked up at him.

'Doesn't seem right, eh? A bloke does all that work and training, he ends up with a Datsun. And a bird drops her tweeds and scores a Mustang.' He belched again. 'I'm maintaining my rage,' he said with a straight face.

Opposite the story about the Playmates was an advertisement for a Presbyterian girls school in Toowoomba. On and on it went.

But, not far from where we were playing baseball, the day took a different turn. The senior Redcliffe cricket team was playing Toombul at Oxenham Park. Sandgate Redcliffe had played well the week before and now the Toombul openers took to the crease. They would have voted early that morning so they could concentrate on the cricket. That's what Martin Bedkoherzz would have done. He was a young player, only twenty-two. It would have been his second election. He'd come up from Sydney with a group of players, including Ian Davis and Jeff Thomson, to bolster the Queensland ranks. Ian Davis had opened the batting for Australia and was destined to again, while Jeff Thomson was bowling for Australia against the West Indies in Perth.

Martin Bedkoherzz was a wicketkeeper who could bat, something of an exciting prospect. And as we sat there, the pie-eater, the small businessman and me; and as my father handed out how-to-vote cards for his party, who he thought were ripe for a hammering; across at Oxenham Park the opening bowler for Sandgate Redcliffe, a hardy medium pacer, trundled in and let a short ball go at a 22-year-old on election day.

The batsman misplayed it and was struck on the heart.

On that fine and warm Saturday, Martin Bedkoherzz collapsed. Under the afternoon sun ambulance officers, his team-mates and the opposing players did their best to revive him. He was rushed to hospital. His friend Ian Davis travelled with him in the ambulance.

Bedkoherzz died. The doctors said that blood had entered the pericardial sac surrounding his heart. It was a very rare occurrence.

That night my father returned early from the election do he'd been to.

'Jesus, he got eaten alive. They'll be in for years,' he announced to the house and nobody in particular.

He dumped a bundle of how-to-vote cards on the table. 'Turn on the Lights' boomed from the Liberal Party celebrations on the television.

'Oh here we go,' said Mum.

Malcolm Fraser smiled and raised his arms and nodded his head uncomfortably.

Nobody said anything.

My father broke the silence. 'Did you hear about that poor lad at the cricket today?'

My mum nodded.

'He was a friend of Thommo's you know.' My father meant Jeff Thomson. 'They didn't tell him. Over in Perth. Greg Chappell didn't tell him until the end of the day's play.'

I thought of Mr West saying what a gentleman Greg Chappell was. And then I supposed Mr West was happy with the day. Well, he was a nice man at least.

'He was going to get married too,' said my mother. 'Poor girl.'

My father let out a sigh.

'It was such a beautiful day.'

For no reason at all I thought of Open Sesame, of what he tried to say. Of what he thought. The day was drawing to an end and I imagined him now. What was he doing? Was he still thinking about the mystery? Whatever that was. Was he in bed or was he at the top of Ella Street watching the cars go by in the dark warm night? Maybe he looked across and took in the placard of Gough Whitlam in our drive. The lights of the cars would have shone on Gough briefly and then left him in darkness. He belonged to history now. The traffic light above the telegraph pole hadn't worked all week. There would be a time yet before anyone would turn on the light.

# 2

1976 was a defining year. In a number of ways. I knew this as I looked down at the little plastic man in my hands. He was a Joe. A GI Joe. He had a scar down his right-hand cheek, brown close-together eyes, close-cropped brown hair and a neat, trimmed little beard. He also had a little piece of hair on his chest. According to what was left of the box he arrived in, he was a new era toy from Hasbro, complete with realistic chest *and* facial hair, plus Kung Fu Grip.

That's all Joe had – that and a fetching set of hard plastic aqua blue bathers with a pointy crotch. Emblazoned at the top of his action plastic briefs was a large A. Symbol of Action.

GI Joe didn't have his boots or his green jumpsuit or gun belt anymore. Bruno had eaten them. Bruno was my aunty Rita's epically stupid Weimaraner hunting dog. And apparently he and Joe had a set-to in the kitchen of my aunty's little house at Deception Bay.

'He thought the dolly was food,' my aunty Rita said when she gave me the GI Joe action 'dolly'.

'Food?' I asked. 'Why?'

'Food, well he –' my aunty Rita pointed to GI Joe, 'was on the table next to the Dinki-Di dog biscuits.'

I looked at her as she lit a fag and then down at Bruno.

She took a puff and then sighed as if she were talking to an idiot. Well, she was talking to me. 'Bruno got confused, and I suppose the dolly was quite tasty. You like a tasty fellow, don't you, Bruno?'

Bruno was tied to a tree in the front yard of my parents' house. He wasn't allowed in because he would see our dog, or smell our cat, and go mental. He stared back with pallid, unblinking blue eyes. He looked noble in a really stupid way.

My aunty Rita had bought a ticket in a door prize at the bowling club in Deception Bay and had come up with Joe. 'Didn't think you'd really be interested in him, but then when Bruno got stuck in I couldn't really give him to the simple kiddies' bin. Can you find a use for him?'

I looked down at the slightly mauled, but still realistically haired GI Joe and knew that I was too old for him. He wasn't my type. I was starting to leave action figures and the like behind.

Only a year or two before I had wished and hoped for a Steve Austin *Six Million Dollar Man* action doll, but he had never materialised in a Christmas stocking or on a birthday. This was a toy based on the ludicrous television show about an astronaut who had a crash and was rebuilt as part-robot. He had two mechanical legs, a bionic eye and a bionic right arm and hand. All these robotic arms and eyes and such worked at breathtaking speed and power. Like Bruno on the loose in the house.

'He's the sort of fella you wouldn't want getting friendly in the shower with you,' said my father as we watched Steve Austin bionic his way through a play fight on the television. 'He might get a bit carried away...no over-enthusiastic cyborgs at shower time.'

'Oh that's charming,' said my mother.

'Well, I've got a brother who was in the merchant navy, love...these things happen,' said my father, pointing at Steve Austin on the television.

I never quite got to the bottom of what Lee Majors, the actor playing Steve Austin, or the bionic man and his hyperactive right arm, and my uncle Tommy the merchant marine had in common with each other, but it did not deter me from thinking an action doll would have been quite a thing to have and hold.

But that was then. I looked at Joe now. I was getting too old for this sort of thing – but if the simple kiddies' bin couldn't have him then I supposed I could find some use for him.

So Joe came to live with us at my parents' house. The great thing about Joe was that my father detested him.

The fact that Joe was overtly American didn't help, but I think it was our little plastic friend's appearance – with his close-cropped hair, little beard and tight blue undies-cum-bathers – that caused my father to stare at him with a great deal of distaste. Added to this was that the manic chewing Joe had endured from the jaws of noble Bruno had given him a lopsided smirk.

I don't think my father ever comprehended that Joe came incomplete, without any of his extras.

'Who gave you that bearded thing? Who?' my father asked. And, without waiting for an answer, he rolled on.

'Christ, son, you're going to be as big as a bloody Clydesdale... you don't need to be mucking around with this bloody fella thing, it's only wearing grundies.' He looked at my mother. 'You're not going to give the boy the thing?'

My mum told him that my aunt, her sister, had given it to me because the charity bin at Deception Bay hadn't wanted it.

'What's wrong with it?' she asked my father.

My father stared at me.

'He's got something that no one else wants! Jesus wept.'

'What's wrong with...it's nothing...put dolly in the bin if you don't want him,' said my aunty Rita

'Oh poor old Joe,' cooed my mother, 'don't put him in the bin.'

'Poor old Joe, my arse... GI Joan more like it. The bin's the best place for him,' muttered my father.

'I quite like him,' I said, for no particular reason other than I thought it might annoy my father.

'Jeeeesuuuus,' breathed my father. 'Watch what you do with the bloody thing, you pie-can.'

I didn't really intend to do anything with GI Joe but I didn't want to tell my father that for it would put the handbrake on some fun. I was in early adolescence and provoking a rise from a parent was a worthwhile use of my time.

I read from the crumpled pack for a little bit of inspiration. 'I'm going to have action-packed adventure with a rugged adventure...' I stopped for Bruno's fangs had chewed away any further inspiration from the packaging. So I added in a token of acknowledgment to my aunty Rita, 'Dolly.'

My mum and aunty laughed. My father glowered.

'We're going to have adventures in the pool, me and my dolly.'

'What is wrong with you, son? You're not going to take that thing to the pool?'

'Well, he is in his bathers,' said my aunty Rita.

'Aren't they his underpants?' piped my mother. 'I think they're underpants.'

'Well he fills them out quite nicely, but he really doesn't have much to be proud about.'

'Oh, come on, turn it up,' said my father.

'Well, why would they go to all the bother? He's not like Howard Keel and his tights in *Kiss Me Kate*... what do they say?'

Nobody had any idea who 'they' were or what they would say.

'Howard was packing heat.' Both the sisters laughed.

'They have got a little belt on them,' I said, holding Joe up and pointing towards the A on his blue bathers-cum-undies.

My father looked at me and did something with his eyebrows and thrust his head forward in what was meant to be a non-verbal warning.

I stopped pointing at the A. My father's head and eyebrows settled back down. Then I tapped the A again.

'You are a pair of arseparts, you and that hairy little sod,' said my father, shaking his head.

I threw Joe, or GI Joan as he also became known depending on who was mentioning him, down on a table outside the front door. I had no intention of taking him with me to the Redcliffe War Memorial Swimming Pool.

Usually we went down to the beach for a swim, or to the jetty to jump and dive, but the pool was the attraction at the moment. It was the time of the Montreal Olympics and all the talk on the radio and telly was of Steven Holland, the current world 1500 metre swimming champion, Australia's only certainty for a gold medal in the pool. Only certainty of any gold really.

His smiling face would peer from newspapers, his frizzy blond hair shining in the black and white photos.

The fact that Steve Holland came from Queensland was an added incentive. A local boy. The plan was to charge up and down the lanes at Redcliffe War Memorial Swimming Pool and appear capable of Olympic feats. But then reality would hit and I ended up bombing off the blocks and trying to impress myself as much as the girls who lay lathered in oil, sunbaking on the grass.

I would walk along the fence by the special school, whose charity bin GI Joe was never to grace, and smell the coconut oil. Some of the girls were my age and some were older, but none wore anything to protect themselves – no sunblock, only suntan oil. Occasionally one would carefully adjust a strap or pull a bikini bottom to get a better tan. But mostly they lay and talked in the sun. Other girls just did what we boys did, giggled and laughed and jumped in the water.

What the girls were actually thinking and doing was unknown to me, for I never spoke to them. I may have been over GI Joe but I wasn't up to the stage of engaging in spoken communication with females.

Getting close enough to catch a waft of the tanning oil was about as far as it went.

No male body, young or old, wore racing Speedos for they were considered to be too daggy. It was board shorts or footy shorts. And any thoughts of standing on the starting blocks trying to be Steve Holland, or the Superfish as he was called by the fat television reporters in bad suits reporting from Montreal, was only held for a short time. Being a gold medal winner, or a certain winner, was all very well for Superfish Steve but even he looked a bit of a dag in his pouchy swimmers.

Only the old men wobbling up and down the concrete paths wore the budgie smugglers, their enormous stomachs cascading over the briefs.

And even though there was a certain glamour attached to the idea of swimming fast and standing on a dais, being a swimming champion seemed like too much hard work.

My mother would shake her head at Norman May as he would build himself into a lather about how all of Australia was willing the Superfish to succeed.

'That'd be right. Old tubby-guts bangs on about the poor boy, but who's up at the crack of dawn training and being yelled at by those coaches? Not Australia, just those kids.'

The Redcliffe pool was run by one of 'those coaches'. Arthur Cusack was an Olympic swimming coach and some Saturday mornings you would see him in his broad-brimmed hat and checked shirt roaring at kids in the water.

I didn't mind the yelling but he always seemed to be so angry. It cut through the early morning light as he screamed at some thrashing child in the water.

I asked Gary, a mate from school who was coached by Arthur, if he was ever frightened by all the shouting and noise. Gary was a quiet boy and his dad was a gentle soul who worked in the National Bank.

'No, I don't think so. He yells because you can't hear well when your head is underwater,' said Gary.

'Do you hear him when you are underwater?'

Gary thought a bit. 'No, no. I guess that's why he shouts louder.'

That made some sort of sense to me, but I wondered why it was that so many coaches seemed to yell so much. It seemed there were a few occupations that required you to yell: maths teachers, the actors in the bad gladiator movies we liked to watch on Saturday afternoons, German dictators and Olympic swimming coaches.

Still they were just voices in the background for the Superfish. Mr Cusack and his like could prowl up and down the lanes and growl all they liked, the real story was the athlete.

Steve Holland was only eighteen years old. He was at the back-end of his adolescence and I was at the threshold of mine. Both of us stood on the starting blocks of an Olympic pool. We were both Queenslanders. And there the resemblance ended. But I knew enough about him to feel some type of affinity as I stood upon the blocks in my banana-yellow Stubbies.

It wasn't such a jump to picture myself in Montreal deciding to swim sans goggles in my unique Made-in-Queensland attire. Nearly thirteen, a few pimples on the way, a nice boofy haircut, I was the perfect example of a pipe-cleaner thin, milk-white Olympic hero.

And why wouldn't you want to be Steve Holland? He was a hero. He'd won just about everything in sight – the world championship, the Commonwealth Games – and broken world records surrounded him. He'd brought the time for the 1500 metres close to the fifteen-minute barrier. The longer he swam, the faster he went.

And just as well, for Australia needed him. The more the Olympic Games wore on, the more the fat men in bad coats bleated in their reports from Montreal that Australians weren't winning. We didn't look like winning a lucky dip.

For the first time in a long time there was no new Olympic champion from Australia. No champion from some country town or some pleasant suburb with a beaming smile to grace the morning papers or television news. No shots of happy parents cheering them on at home, no first interviews with old friends or school teachers who remembered him or her from the early years.

Australia wasn't used to not winning gold at the Olympics. There was a seemingly endless club of gold medal owners from previous Olympiads, and the fear started to spread that maybe this time none would be added.

All the girls wanted to be Nadia Comaneci, the Romanian gymnast who bounded and leapt with muscular grace and perfection.

'She's quite incredible,' said Mrs Lewdy, a teacher at school who had a habit of trying to masquerade her nose-picking with a lace-hanky-clad finger, which earned her the title of Mrs Lewdy, Picker Bewdy. 'She's much nicer than that Olga Korbut woman. Nadia is so graceful in an immodest way,' added Picker Bewdy. 'It's hard to believe she's a communist. It may be the injections,' she added thoughtfully.

There were already rumours and reports, courtesy of the chubby men in bad jackets, about the size and power of Iron Curtain athletes, especially the 'communist lasses'.

If we weren't winning there must be a reason and drugs and gulag training camps were obvious choices. Australia wanted a winner – more than it may have thought it did – to prove that we could compete and succeed on the big stage against the world. Things had been a bit dry recently.

We hadn't had a Wimbledon tennis champion since Evonne Goolagong in 1971. John Newcombe might do all right on the grass at Kooyong but the new tennis champions seemed to come from America, the land of GI Joe/Joan, or from odd countries like Sweden and Romania, even Argentina.

Thank goodness for the cricketers.

But all the girls, and maybe even some of the boys, wanted to be Nadia Comaneci, with her perfect ten performances.

Even at the pool the odd girl would be doing Comaneci-inspired cartwheels and round-offs. I didn't like some of the dives the tough boys would attempt, because they were more like the flashy bits from the floor routines of the male gymnasts than the more utilitarian bomb.

If a degree of difficulty was required then you could always opt for the Horsey dive. It was a noted variation on the bomb, only one leg was bent and gripped to the chest while the other leg was left straight as the diver soared through the air and emitted a scream. But fashion, it seems, was moving and even though some of the tough boys didn't look that keen they would try to do dives with words that until 1976 had no meaning whatsoever, things like half-pikes and triple and backward somersaults.

Picker Bewdy didn't like the male gymnasts because, 'They are too full of muscle and unpleasantness. They don't smile and they don't believe in God.' She picked a bit and then, in a considered tone that teachers in bad television shows use when something wise is being said, added, 'There is nothing wrong with being a peasant, but not believing in God will end in no good – no matter how many gold medals you win.'

My father was unsure about what was happening.

'These buggers are strong,' he said as some muscled and unsmiling Eastern Bloc athlete twirled and twisted on some rings. 'But I don't know.'

'What don't you know, Col?' said Mum.

After bit of thought my old man came up with the conclusion that, 'They're too bloody European. Look at 'em. They run round in these bloody funny little pyjama things and leap about to this weird music.'

The whole process was something you did inside a hall, not outdoors on an oval like a proper game.

'It's more of a circus act than a sport…it's not like football.' Then my father thought of Nadia Comaneci. He nodded in approval. 'She's built like a bloody halfback, lovely girl.'

But there was still the Superfish to keep Australia and the newspapers busy. A countdown was on until Steve Holland faced off with the Americans in the 1500 metres.

The great thing about the growing fascination with gymnastics though, was that the muscled frowners from Montreal had a more than passing resemblance to GI Joe/Joan. This annoyed my father no end.

Despite our best efforts to let GI Joe/Joan fade into the pleasant mess of our house, my father had the happy knack of stumbling across the action man dolly.

'Jesus wept! What is this bastard doing?' my father roared as Joe appeared in his study, rakishly perched on top of two Makita sanders. He'd been tossed there by my mother and had landed in a relaxed, cross-legged pike, with his fuzzy, realistic hair shining in the light.

'Do stop carrying on about poor Joe – what is the matter with you?' said my mother.

'I don't like beards and I don't like fellas smirking at me; even if they are plastic bloody dwarves,' answered my father.

This of course opened up a whole new avenue of delight, and we made sure that Joe/Joan followed my old man.

His Kung Fu Grip enabled the placer to perch Joe quite successfully on the back of the dog's collar. Or on the toilet-paper holder.

'Get this fella out of here, I'm not wiping in anger with him here!'

On the back of my father's chair at the dining table or, best still, on the teapot.

Joe/Joan even had a tool around the peninsula on the tray of my father's truck where his Kung Fu Grip managed to cling long enough to deliver a cement-mixer to Woody Point.

The extra passenger went unnoticed until I pointed him out in the afternoon.

'Christ, you silly gimp of a boy, don't hang this bearded voodoo bastard near me again.'

And my father picked Joe/Joan up by his little hands and flung him away as he might a slimy fish or reptile.

My father shuddered, 'Oh, he's got clammy mitts that bugger.'

The only time my old man had any delight out of GI Joe/Joan was when my mate Reg Worth and I rigged up a piece of fishing line from the back veranda down to the shed, put a coathanger over the line, wrapped Joe's clammy mitts around the hanger and made a flying fox for Joe to shudder down.

As Joe wobbled down, his legs were splayed, as Picker Bewdy would have it, in a variety of graceful but immodest poses – and we would merrily shoot at Joe with Reg's air rifle.

'Get his bloody legs together, for Christ's sake!' And then when Joe continued to fly there was a bit more glee in the air.

'Take that, you hairy pie-can! Go on give him another one!' chortled my old man.

Again and again, Joe would be hit but he'd never fall. Never flinch. This gave Joe/Joan a new name. 'Jesus, you have to hand it to him, he's doing the Ken Mackay,' approved my father. This was in reference to a piece of sporting heroism during the 1960–61 West Indies cricket tour of Australia. Queensland all-rounder Ken Mackay had taken the last two balls from Wes Hall, the fastest bowler in the world, on the body to ensure that no wicket would be lost. That was from another time though, the black-and-white age.

Ken/Joe/Joan, as he finally became known, entered some sort of uneasy truce with my father as the talk gave way to the 1500 metres. It had become clear the race would be the only chance of a gold medal in Montreal that we in Australia would have.

It wasn't a matter of everyday thought but it did seem to dominate mild conversation, or the sort of chat that you would have to pass the time of day. With people at petrol stations say, or in the shops.

'Isn't it awful about the way we're doing at the Olympics?'

'It was the starter's fault that Raelene Boyle broke in the hundred metres.'

'Held her too long.'

'Aren't those gymnasts amazing?'

'Well, they're not normal really.'

'Lots of drugs.'

'But Nadia is lovely.'

'The hockey team couldn't even beat New Zealand!'

'Well at least there's Steve Holland.'

My father had sensed something was in the wind. 'These poor sods from the Commie places are like the Yanks – they do nothing but run and jump and swim and bounce. It's their job. They don't need to do paper rounds or mow lawns like our mob. No wonder we can't win a chook raffle.'

Malcolm Fraser even bought into the whole schemozzle. He met President Ford in Washington and then tacked on a visit to the athletes at the Olympic village, an added little extra that not many people could see the value in.

'Well, at least Whitlam wouldn't have done that,' said Dad.

'Well, there are no ruins in Montreal for him to lecture people about,' said my mother.

Malcolm was having an interesting time in power. He was going to try to control inflation – a gift, not of the world economy and the oil crisis of the early seventies, but, handily enough for him, of Gough and his merry band of spendthrifts.

So he ran the party line ad nauseam but at the same time Vietnamese refugees, or Boat People as they were commonly known, were welcomed into Australia on Fraser's insistence. Even though sentiments like those expressed by the old men who would sit out by the jetty café in the mornings and mutter, 'Why did we fight the war to let them all come here?' were widespread, Fraser accepted a responsibility of the involvement in war and some of its consequences.

'He is a funny bastard, Mal,' my father offered. 'He does something like that but then he wants to turn the clock back.'

His government changed the national song back to 'God Save the Queen' as a part of its dismantling of the excesses of Gough Whitlam. So Fraser looked quite at home in his suits defending the monarch.

'Oh it's all politics,' according to Mum.

Picker Bewdy thought he was strong and decent and my aunty Rita liked him because he was a farmer.

The one thing that I couldn't understand was why Australia had replaced one Harry High Pants, or Choko Charlie, with another. Whitlam had always worn his pants high and Fraser had a similar sartorial trait as far as trousers went. Instead of the general all-round waist-choking favoured by the bookish Whitlam, Fraser had an awkward sling approach that defines a certain type of person.

His pants went high over his stomach, almost to his belly button, but then fell away to kiss the top of his arse. In the words of my father, he was ripe for a hungry bum.

'Fellas who wear their dacks like that,' my father said as we watched television footage of Big Mal waiting endlessly outside the Olympic village after being frisked by security, 'get their trousers chewed by the cheeks of their arse.'

My father's idea was that this sort of person was usually a bit shy and awkward. I looked at Fraser as he waited outside the Olympic Village for admittance. He had waited a while and he smiled thinly. He did look a little shy.

'Look how he's standing!' yelled my father. Fraser stood with one leg slightly bent, his suit top open with his hands on his hips. Though his hands weren't perched on his hips like the figures in a Russell Drysdale painting, or the Australian cricket team's slips cordon, with their thumb and forefingers cocked on the hips as they leant to one side.

Fraser stood with flat palms with the fingers pointing down to his feet. I had seen pictures in books of old governors and dukes and whatnot standing like that in the portraits. And Fraser stood like this.

'He's nervous, people like that clench their guts a lot. Their bums follow suit.'

'Oh, Colin,' said my mother.

'Listen, I've seen things. I know men.'

'Were you in the merchant marine too?' I asked stupidly.

'You are an arsepart sometimes.' My father shook his head.

The idea of Fraser being shy and awkward was one that I hadn't heard before. He was always portrayed as a lantern-jawed blue blood from a big farm in Victoria. A would-be aristocrat, but as I looked I remembered another person who stood like that: a lonely boy at school who would pretend to talk into a radio microphone at lunchtime. He'd pick up a stone and clench it in his hands and away he would go.

If you went near him to pick up an errant footy that had bounced his way he would turn and whisper, 'Going silent, over. Radio silence needed, over.' He'd turn away and stand with his palms flat on his hips, save for the rock, until you walked away and then he'd fire up again.

'Channel open, Steve, go ahead.'

He would stand by the fence and rabbit away. God knows who he was talking to, maybe Steve Austin from the *Six Million Dollar Man* or some other imaginary friend, but he was bright and very good at maths and wasn't considered simple by anybody.

But in sport he would stand like Malcolm Fraser was standing now, alone and a little nervous, wondering what would happen to him.

When Fraser nodded his head up and down he all of a sudden did look uncomfortable and a little lost.

'This fella,' said my father, nodding to the television as Fraser walked amongst the athletes, 'should have waited. He's never going to get over how he got there. Him and that drunken arse Kerr. It'll always haunt him. And he's got form for farting about – he whiteanted John Gorton and all that led to was Billy Bloody McMahon.'

Fraser didn't look haunted as he sat talking to the athletes. Maybe nonplussed. There was no medal winner to congratulate and slap on the shoulder. But when he told the athletes that it was more important to compete than to win and wave your medals about he got it with both barrels from the Australian representatives.

They were under-funded and now ill-equipped to compete with the world. No gold medals, no glory. If they had the money they could win.

Fraser sat and listened. He was the head of a government that was trying to slash spending and rein in inflation and the perceived wantonness of the Whitlam years. The Razor Gang, a group of his ministers in charge of cutting public spending, was beginning to sharpen the blade and Fraser could have sat with the athletes, nodded awkwardly and then gone.

But he didn't. He came out talking about a review into the lack of success by the Olympic team and committed the government to uphold Australia's proud sporting culture. The best way this could be done according to the review was to set up the Australian Institute of Sport, an elite training facility.

Our proud sporting culture, it seemed, meant success and, without that, having a go seemed not to really matter.

Success.

Australia wanted it. And when Steve Holland the Superfish swam we would have it. It was live via satellite and in colour. He stood on the blocks, in the fastest lane, lane 5, looking much smaller than the two Americans, Hackett and Goodell. As he waited for the gun I wondered what he felt.

It was nerve-racking enough pretending to be him at the Redcliffe War Memorial Swimming Pool, hoping you wouldn't bellyflop into the water in yellow Stubbies in front of the girls with the suntan oil, but actually being Steve Holland must have been another thing altogether.

He must have known that the country, or what he thought the country was, namely the newspaper headlines and the fat fellows in bad jackets and microphones, and the yelling coaches, wanted him to win.

I sat there behind my father and family, and prised Ken/Joe/Joan's hands open and clipped him onto my nose. I tapped my father on the shoulder. He turned and looked at me for a long time with the action man hanging from my nose.

'Christ almighty, do you have to buggerise around at a time like this? Really!' He shook his head and turned around and clapped his hands.

I let Joe fall onto the floor.

I got a funny feeling in my tummy. It seemed like there was no noise around the pool and then the gun went. The American Hackett took off and led, and Holland followed. He never seemed to have followed anybody before and he didn't seem to want to this time.

'I hope he's careful, the Yanks will gang up on him,' said my mother.

I wondered if Steve Holland's mother felt the same thing. They'd be watching this now, I thought. Watching him splash up and down the lane live via satellite. He could have been on Mars really. But there he was on the telly.

Holland swam along with Hackett for what seemed like an age, and the laps finished and time stretched and all of a sudden he seemed to have the measure of Hackett.

Then Goodell swam up to take Hackett's place and on they swam. There was no big kick and no big end. The last two laps were agony.

'Oh no,' cried my sister.

'Come on, son!' yelled my father.

'Come on, come on!' shouted my mother.

But he couldn't. He had done all he could. The Americans swept past him at the end to touch him into third.

All three men had swam faster than they ever had before. Nobody said much, not even the commentator. Save for the bold statement about Goodell as Steve Holland leant on the lane ropes and waited to shake hands. 'That's what a winner looks like!'

Steve Holland smiled and ducked his head underwater.

I cried. Holland seemed to be trying so hard to be a good sport. It matters that you compete, Fraser had said. Well, he had. But what about our proud sporting culture?

My father stood up and looked at the television.

'You poor little sod... God bless ya.' And he pointed gently to Steve Holland.

He turned around and looked down at me. He didn't say anything but patted me gently on the head and then went to walk the dog.

GI Joe smirked up at me from the floor. I picked him up and flung him away towards the old piano.

Apparently when Steve Holland got out from the pool, his coach Bill Sweetnam turned his back on him. What Holland must have felt is anybody's guess. The headlines didn't crucify him and the fat men with the microphones didn't say he didn't try. He just wasn't good enough.

So he was forgotten, but never allowed to forget. He wasn't Superfish anymore, he was just a bloke who wasn't good enough.

He was only eighteen. He never swam competitively again and, save for the odd surf-lifesaving carnival, he drifted away from my life.

The next day I stood at the pool. There weren't that many people there. A girl I knew from school was doing something over by the barbeque that was inspired by Nadia Comaneci. The last time I had seen this girl in her bathers was in little school at a swim lesson. Then she looked no different to me really. Things were changing. I stared a little longer than I should have and she pulled herself up from a running jump and adjusted the straps on her bikini. She didn't smile at me, but then she didn't turn away.

Well, there weren't that many people at the pool.

I stood in my yellow Stubbies. Took a deep breath and started running for the pool.

No standing on the blocks like the Superfish and thrashing down the pool.

I tried desperately to remember the stern-faced gymnasts in their funny, tight little costumes and raced across the concrete pool surface.

What I ended up doing is beyond the powers of description. I contorted my skinny white body into some attempt at an acrobatic leap and I knew as I fell through the air in my yellow Stubbies – which had the unhappy effect of splaying my prepubescent balls to either side of the heavy crotch seam – that I was in trouble.

Hanging in the air I had a feeling of having let down Steve Holland. His coach and his country may have turned their backs on him, but I could have done a little better.

He was eighteen years old, near the end of his adolescence, and his life would be haunted by that race in Montreal, by his failure to uphold our sporting culture.

I was nearly thirteen and my testicles, freshly sporting hair that looked less realistic than GI Joe's, smashed into the water and ended, it seemed, at either side of my ears.

I stayed underwater for as long as I could. My stomach stinging and face reddening. The girl wouldn't be looking anymore.

Things were changing all right.

Success and winning, and looking the part, were what mattered in 1976. Floating in the pool, for some mad reason, I said to myself, 'Live via satellite.' The bubbles plopped past my ears and broke emptily into the air.

# 3

There wasn't much of a yard to mow. It was your basic green-carpeted southeast Queensland suburban lawn. Bland and bare. Chook wire ran along three sides but there was no fence at the front. There weren't too many clumps of growth that could hide toads. Not much to really do to it, but for three years I mowed the lawns for a little bit of cash and, on occasion, some warm orange cordial courtesy of Mrs Glazier.

Mrs Glazier was an immense woman who wore vast dark dresses and had a moustache. She spoke with a soft, sibiliant English accent. Her eyesight was bad and the images on her colour television were all tinged with a lurid algae green. Certainly Rick McCosker looked green. In fact he looked like he came from Mars as we watched old footage of him walking out to bat in the 1977 Centenary Test. Him and his broken jaw. And his baggy green cap covered the great egg of his bandages.

'Oh, he was brave, wasn't he?' whispered Mrs Glazier.

McCosker's jaw had been broken in the first innings and now he had come out to bat in the second. His captain, the gentlemanly Greg Chappell, had tried to stop him but McCosker would have none of it.

My family and I had watched the test a few months earlier, and when McCosker came out to bat my father had clapped his hands.

'Now that, that bloke there, that's a man.'

'Colin, do you have to yell with your mouth full?' said my mother.

'Sorry, but it's more than that poor sod can do! Well done you.' He pointed a finger at the television.

I looked at McCosker, eyes downcast, his awkward country gait emphasised by the ungainly cricket pads and tight trousers. He didn't showboat. His reaction to the crowd singing 'Oh Rick McCosker' to the tune of 'Waltzing Matilda' was to gently raise his bat and continue waddling to the crease.

He may not have been the best player, or the flashiest, but he was certainly the bravest.

'Showboating' was the term that my father gave to acts of lairising or showing off. Of letting people know that what you had done was good and important. Of carrying on like a pork chop.

We'd already seen a bit of showboating at the Centenary Test with the wonderful fast bowler Dennis Lillee and his performances for the umpires. He may have been brave bowling with his bad back and bruised feet, but he was still a showboater.

In fact the showboating began when the former English and Australian cricket captains had assembled side by side at the start of the test.

And if anyone needed any evidence that cricket was a game of the suburbs then there it was in the faces of the Australian captains. None of them would have been out of place walking down the streets of our neighbourhood. All bluff blokes, even the white-haired Richie Benaud. Perhaps Richie may have had a wine down at the bowls club instead of a beer at the RSL, but he would still have fitted snugly into our life. In fact, any of them could have walked up our drive to hire something from my father's hire service. It would most likely have been party equipment because a few did look white collar – especially the Victorians like Lindsay Hassett and Bill Johnston, although Bill Lawry had a tradesman's look about him that my father approved of.

Don Bradman, my father thought, would be the sort of fellow to hire a sander for a little bit of home renovation and then return it in better condition than it had been when he borrowed it.

'A mysterious bugger, The Don,' he said.

But Ian Chappell had blotted his copybook.

'Oh Christ, will you look at him!' moaned my mother.

'Oh son…that's not up to speed…oh dear,' said my father, for he liked Ian Chappell.

He shook his head. 'Why is the silly bastard wearing a safari suit?'

It was a question worth asking.

'Maybe he's in the Labor Party,' I offered.

That made some sense to my father and he considered it for a moment, then he shook his head.

'No, no-no-no-no. Christ. A green safari suit.'

Even my father had stopped wearing these creations.

'Oh Ian, you look like you work at the pawnbrokers.' The pawnbrokers was a hock shop cum real estate office in Deception Bay that was run by a group of shifty looking men who wore aviator glasses, had moustaches that seemed to be glued on and all drove Sunbirds – cars that made the Cortina, universally loathed as the poor man's Torana, look good.

That is what Ian Chappell looked like.

'A green safari suit,' said my father again.

'And sunglasses,' added my mother.

My father nodded sadly. 'And sunglasses.' He sighed. 'Why'd you have to go and showboat, Ian? He looks like a goose.'

The safari suit did look a little lurid. It looked like he was dressed to be on Mrs Glazier's television.

But he wasn't. Rick McCosker was still waddling away until he was abruptly replaced by the image of Kerry Packer, the 39-year-old owner of the television station.

A voiceover told us that cricket had gone from the glory of the Centenary Test to the controversy of Kerry Packer in a few short months.

Not to mention a hiding by the English in the Ashes.

Kerry Packer, with a wide fleshy face and watchful eyes, looked at the journalist off-screen like some great predator, half smiled and said softly, 'I'm just interested in good quality cricket.'

I watched Kerry Packer while Mrs Glazier poured me an orange cordial to celebrate my agreeing to mow her carpet of lawn occasionally.

Mrs Glazier could hardly see as evidenced by the thick dark spectacles she wore. She filled a glass, with the white outline of a Cobb and Co coach embossed on it, with water from the hot tap and I drank my first in a long line of warm orange cordials.

I said thanks, for it seemed impolite to point out that the drink was anything but cool and refreshing.

Kerry Packer looked out from the television with unflappable coolness and seemed to mock me with his steady gaze.

Mrs Glazier's poor eyesight was also evidenced the next day as my father flapped his hand up and down at her from the cabin of his truck while intermittently giving the thumbs-up sign.

'She's a lovely woman but, by Christ, she looks like she's wearing welding goggles,' he muttered as he gave me a lift to school. 'Do you think she saw me? Blind as a bat.'

'Mum says she puts sugar in her sweet potato mash.'

'You what?'

'Mrs Glazier puts sugar in her sweet potato mash. She gave Mum a recipe for it.'

'I'm talking about her eyesight for Christ's sake – not what she puts in her mashed potatoes,' my father fumed.

'Sweet potato,' I added.

My father kept driving but took both hands off the steering wheel and pointed at me with his forefingers, as if he were an Australian Rules goal umpire signalling a goal. As he did this he cupped the steering wheel in his knees and proceeded to drive.

'Now look you, don't go shirking off and doing a half-arsed effort because she can't see through those beer bottles she's wearing. Make a go of it...do a good job and maybe there'll be other lawns you could do. Who knows where it'll stop?'

I wondered what my father meant. Did he think I could become a professional lawn mower man? Was that my future path? I thought of people who mowed lawns. They usually worked at the council or were grumpy school janitors. I didn't really see myself there. And then there was my father. He would occasionally mow lawns, with incendiary results.

My father believed that there were some people who were too lazy to do their own lawns.

'Don't ask me why but there are sods out there who'll pay you money to push a mower around for twenty minutes. They want a specialist service.'

For a while my father would add this to his entrepreneurial basket, turning up at people's backyards for 'twenty minutes of specialist service' with his squadron of mower machines.

'I'll just whip out and do a lawn, back in a tick,' my father would cheerfully say, and anyone within earshot would roll their eyes, for the twenty minutes would deepen into an hour and a half, and on some occasions a whole afternoon.

It was because of the squadron of mowers. These contraptions were cannibalised from bits and pieces of different mowers, found objects and things that were probably never mowers in the first place.

The squadron ranged from something George Jetson might use on a Saturday night for a bit of fun, to an appliance Dr Frankenstein knocked up in his garden shed in his spare time, to things resembling the odd machines used to prepare France for the Allied invasion at Normandy in World War II – great threshing machines that would explode landmines in wallowing clouds of smoke.

The squadron consisted of two types of mowers: rotary-started mowers and cord-pull mowers.

On the rotary mower a little handle at the top would be turned and slapped down and the machine would leap into life. Well, that was the theory. My father would hunch squatting over the mower with his great body quivering as he wound and wound the handle.

A little sigh of mechanical intent would be released by the mower and then it would shudder into silence.

The 'Fartin' Bastard' it became known as. But, without a doubt, the top-shelf moment was when my father would start the chorded Victor Rover. A string would be pulled to crank the motor and then lever controls would be manipulated to govern the speed of the mower.

My father would heave and yank and pull with all his might and then attack the lever like some bad actor in an old film as if he were fighting the controls of a spacecraft.

And, like a bad actor, he would speak to the machine.

'Oh come on you swine of a thing...'

Try to reason with it.

'Come on, Victor old mate, there's a lad, come on. Come ON. Come ON!'

He'd yank at string.

'Start, you bastard, start...work AHHHHH!'

Another yank and he'd look like he was a hammer thrower in the Olympics.

He would yell so much at the machines that some of his customers thought he was talking to another person, this Victor fellow, and would peer out through their windows to see who the man providing their specialist service was yelling at.

I thought about all this as we drove to school but I didn't say anything. Then I nodded in the way teenagers nod when they aren't listening. A blank-eyed bob of the head. Without a great deal of thought I asked, 'Would Kerry Packer mow lawns?'

I didn't know if my father had heard me.

'You've got to go easy on the mowers because if you fart around you'll bugger them up... Why would you put sugar in sweet potato?' He scratched his head and held the wheel again. After a while he said in an empty voice, 'No, son, Kerry Packer wouldn't mow lawns. Why would he when he can buy a whole sport?'

Packer had wanted to buy the broadcast rights to the test cricket because across the world televised sport was a magnet for advertising dollars. Packer had offered the Australian Cricket Board more than the ABC for the television rights, but the cricketing establishment decided that transmissions of the national game should stay with the national broadcaster. Instead of buying the broadcast rights, Packer came up with the idea of buying the players and, therefore, the game.

So during the time that I mowed Mrs Glazier's garden carpet, there were two cricketing competitions: the Packer-led circus and the establishment tests.

Packer said that taking over the game was easy because the Australian Cricket Board didn't pay the players a fraction of what they were worth.

He had a point. The board was starting to make a lot of money from the game and passing very little of it back to the players. And so the parsimonious nature of the board's financial offers, plus the conservatism of their administration, rendered them powerless against the deep pockets of Packer's media empire.

The players were basically amateurs in a sport that was making a profit, and with the promise of more money to be made, why wouldn't they want a larger piece of the pie?

Up until then the best that professional athletes seemed to get from television was what they received at the end of interviews on shows like *Sports Scene* and *Wide World of Sport*. After a panel discussion the smiling host Rod Gallegos would turn to the sporty type and say with a wink, 'You won't be leaving us empty-handed. You've got the Addy-das sports bag, the Hutton's "Don't Argue" Footy Franks, a tube of Dencorub, a jar of professional-strength Staminade sports drink, a pair of VYI sunglasses, a dinner for two at the Top of the Town and a night at Dirty Dick's Medieval Theatre Restaurant.'

This glowing assortment of treasure was shown on camera, and surely no man could feel less than a king with such booty. But overnight, with the age of Packer, people could see that it would soon be possible to earn your living from sport.

It was about appreciating people's worth in the market of life and this is where Packer understood the time.

If the Olympic athletes could complain to Malcolm Fraser and demand more financial assistance then it seemed that cricket and other sports could embrace the idea of paying athletes.

There were some players who initially resisted the temptations of Packer's money, but it quickly became apparent what the upshot of all the upheaval would be.

The idea that one man could own a whole sport was what seemed to tarnish the game in my father's eyes.

It was fine for Dennis Lillee to pose, pump up his heroics and immerse himself in the role of demon fast bowler, but how could one man own the deeds of Rick McCosker?

'You can have all the money in the world but you can't own what that fella McCosker did,' my father said as he drove me to school. '"Cause he didn't do it for the money, he did it for us, son. Because he thought it was the right thing to do.'

Still, it didn't stop me from thinking it would be great if Kerry Packer asked me to join his circus. I remembered his great impassive green face from Mrs Glazier's telly. While my father banged on about Rick McCosker, I was suddenly shaking Kerry's hand and signing up for countless thousands of Hutton's Footy Franks and jars of Staminade. We posed for the press photographers and shared a celebratory warm orange cordial, me and Kerry – and Mrs Glazier. In fact the two had begun to morph into each other and were constantly linked within my mind, the mention of one momentarily flinging up a mental image of the other.

My father must have decided that he had found a rich vein of metaphorical life-message gold with Rick McCosker for he was mining it for all it was worth. He took his hands off the steering wheel and beeped the horn, not to warn other motorists but to announce a new thought. He drove with his knees and spoke with his hands.

'Listen, sunshine, when you think it's all about money, when you think you can do a half-arsed job on that poor woman's lawn, think about Rick McCosker. Think about what he would do...' My father smiled to himself, beeped the horn again and leapt into a rendition of 'Oh Rick McCosker'.

I nodded the adolescent bob of understanding, but it was all for show. I don't think I quite knew what Rick McCosker had to do with mowing Mrs Glazier's lawns but I did note that money, and the chasing and the using of it, were in the air.

The federal treasurer, Phillip Lynch, had produced a budget that, in his own words, was 'rubbery'. He was eventually sacked from Malcolm Fraser's cabinet because of a conflict of interests – the laws he was passing and the properties he was developing had become seemingly intermeshed.

Meanwhile Malcolm Fraser, that bastion of all things establishment and proper, remained manifestly silent on Packer's cricket takeover. This had more to do with the idea that there was no point in making a fuss over something that was likely to put out of joint the nose of a man who owned a vast media conglomerate, including the most successful television network in the country, than taking a stand on what was good and proper for Australian sport culture.

It was an election year after all.

Fraser won the election so comfortably that it was one of the few election nights our television wasn't tuned to the tally room from go to woe.

It wasn't that late into the evening when we sat and watched Fraser's victory announcement. He bore on in his metronomic monotone that he wanted to govern for all Australians no matter what they did or where they were from. He wanted to govern using the things that unite all Australians. He wanted to lead by uniting all Australians. How that was going to happen, and what the things were that were going to unite us, wasn't made clear because Fraser wasn't interested in expounding on them. He looked like he was just going through the motions. He took no questions and disappeared off into the Southern Cross Hotel.

The 1977 election was the last Whitlam would face as leader and he was crushed again, suffocating under the avalanche of votes supporting the Liberals. Their campaign had promised people handfuls of cash back in huge tax cuts, which miraculously never seemed to eventuate after the election.

The carrot was dangled and all the donkeys in the land continued to chase it.

For the first time perhaps, men who didn't actually play the sports they were associated with were becoming the most famous faces within areas of sporting endeavour.

Kerry Packer in cricket. Alan Bond, a self-made millionaire from Perth, was single-handedly, it seemed, attempting to wrest yachting's most famous trophy, the America's Cup, from the clutches of the Newport Yacht Club of Rhode Island, New York. Geoffrey Edelsten, who ran a series of medical clinics in Sydney, had bought the South Melbourne VFL football team, which became the Sydney Swans. He was as likely to have ever played football as I was to start the Fartin' Bastard mower first time to do Mrs Glazier's lawn.

Yet none of these fellows was ever expected to think about what Rick McCosker would have done before they went about their days.

I'm sure that Rick would have carried his swollen jaw with dignity and honesty as he pushed the Fartin' Bastard over Mrs Glazier's grass, but then he would probably have been able to start the bloody thing, using his country common sense to make some sort of order from the monster that my father had created.

I wound and snapped and wound and snapped, but the handle wouldn't do what it was supposed to do. I wound and snapped and my father's voice, though he himself was unseen, carried across the yards. 'Go on so, a bit more Rick McCosker.'

I pictured myself swathed in bandages and had another go and wound and snapped fruitlessly. I was lucky to even get a fart out of it. After constant and largely inept attempts to engage the rotary I happened on the idea that, like some of my family's dodgy vehicles, perhaps the Fartin' Bastard could be jump-started.

For the next twenty or so minutes I ran up and down the length of Mrs Glazier's yard thrusting and wrestling with the Fartin' Bastard, trying to coax some breath into its engine.

Then I tried the front yard, thinking that a slope would aid my efforts.

I tripped over, but didn't fall, making my momentum even greater. I looked up and across the road there was Open Sesame standing stock still, staring. At me. I looked and he looked. I was going to say something but couldn't be bothered. He seemed to be going to say something, but instead he slowly shook his head.

I renewed my efforts to show up Open Sesame.

Nothing happened and I collapsed upon the seat in the little concrete patio, where the wet-weather clothesline was strung loosely with some very old wooden pegs.

Mrs Glazier came lumbering up and in her hand was a glass of orange cordial

'Oh you have done a good job. Thank you so very much.' And in her other hand was a ten-dollar note.

'Oh yes, very neat, you're a good worker.'

I looked down at her yard and saw no difference, save for a collection of desperate, swerving lines made by the mower and my feet where I had screamed across the grass.

I could have told her I hadn't done the job. I should have told her I hadn't done the job. What, I asked myself, would Rick McCosker do?

Or should I make the most of this opportunity?

I took the ten-dollar note and told myself that at least I had never mentioned that the cordial was warm.

It started a nasty habit of claiming money from Mrs Glazier that I never really earned. There were some days, when I had the more reliable Victor Rover, that I actually did cut the grass. And on the days when I was after a bit of money I would make sure I chatted to Mrs Glazier. She may have been a bit perplexed by my behaviour, but it made me feel better.

She had a record she liked to play. It was a collection of songs by various singers, but the one she liked best was a song by a man called Bobby Rydell. There was a photo of him on the record sleeve and, true to Mrs Glazier's form with the television, it seemed to be covered in a coloured glaze. An orange wash draped Bobby's face. Perhaps it was his tan. He had enormous hair, a huge flat-top cut. So big you could lay a family-sized pizza on it, and his big teeth were as white as liquid paper. The song he sang was 'Forget Him'.

What would Rick McCosker do?

Bobby sang in his best breathy leagues club vibrato to 'Forget Him'. So I went with Bobby.

It wasn't that I was the only one. Almost everybody knew that kickbacks galore were happening in the Queensland state government under Joh Bjelke-Petersen. His minister for everything, Russ Hinze, was becoming a cult figure with his creative use of public monies. In the middle of nowhere a beautiful sealed road had been constructed connecting various properties owned by Hinze. Even Phillip Lynch had returned to federal cabinet after a safe enough time had elapsed since the election. He had been replaced as treasurer by a young man who was fond of wearing waistcoats. John Winston Howard.

My friends and I followed suit. We didn't start wearing waistcoats and sporting a comb-over as the federal treasurer did; we started taking opportunities. On the day that Sir Robert Menzies died, surely a metaphor for the end of a certain type of propriety, my friend Peter landed a gift from the gods of opportunism. It was a little ray of sunshine for all of us.

Peter got a job at the Sunshine servo down in Clontarf, which was owned by Mick the Pom and Stan Stan the One-armed Man. They did little and left the staff to run the place.

There were three workers there, Peter and two oddities of humanity called Lobby and Kelvin Mintin. Kelvin would hold forth about how smoking could cure pimples – he smoked like a chimney but his face looked like a meat lover's special; about how afterburners on jet aircraft held spy cameras that checked up on what the council workers were up to; and that he, Kelvin Mintin, had devised the concept of inbuilt obsolescence and had sold it to the Reader's Digest Group.

In other words, he was barking.

He would bang on with so much incessant tripe that Peter would get us to come in and fill a shopping trolley, then walk out as Kelvin banged away. Eventually Kelvin would spot the orphaned, and by now empty, trolley and go and collect it.

'Bloody kids,' he would blurt before going on to the next piece of idiocy.

Nobody seemed to care, least of all Stan Stan the One-armed Man and Pommy Mick. They were too busy in Fortitude Valley to ever look back in anger.

The tobacco trade was always an eager effort engaged in by all, even by those who didn't smoke.

In between the ciggie rack and the fruit and vegies shelf was a perfect doorway of opportunity to pass various items through to the eager hands of friends.

You would go in and start up a coded conversation with Peter or some like-minded matey conspirator.

'Has Paul Hogan been in today?'

'Uh huh,' came the response and then a question. 'How old is he today?'

'Oh he turned twenty-five.'

Through the portal of largesse went a packet of Winfield 25s.

If somebody was after Strop it would be a pack of Winfield Blues.

All the time Kelvin would be talking to Lobby about how if you played Nana Mouskouri records backwards she would 'swear dirty words like in the Exercise-ist'.

If somebody asked after Stuart Wagstaff then a carton of Benson & Hedges would be squeezed through.

As we got older we all needed more money and yet, even when we got part-time jobs down at Coles, the idea of somehow making things work for you was paramount to the cynicism of the age. You did as little as possible, and it was easy to do that on the odd days I was required in the meat area.

A tall man with a limp and the appropriately named Joyce Mutton did most of the work.

I managed to draw a wage without turning up very often, so when a pale hairy man called Eric, who had a habit of shedding long strands of dark hair, took my place one Saturday I could hardly complain.

And there was always Mrs Glazier's lawn.

Even though Mal Fraser was committing Australia to becoming a multicultural nation and began the first transmissions from the Special Broadcasting Service, the world and the drought had begun to close in on Big Mal.

The economy was very much like me and my group of friends. It wasn't really achieving very much at all. We arsed around and generally cruised through the days. At school in economics we would hear strange stirrings of words like 'rationalism' and its relevance to efficiency, and that economics was no longer a social science but was in fact becoming a system based around models and statistics, not society, not people.

Mrs Glazier then became a set inflow of income to me. I provided a service to her. This occurred to me one day when she gave me a warm cordial and some money I hadn't earned from the lawn.

I did sit and chat though and, in this way, I was following the suit of refining the service I was providing. But sometimes even in a perfect economic model something can creep in – a past, a voice of a fleeting memory. Life.

I was ready to chat but instead Mrs Glazier held my hand for a long time. She didn't play Bobby Rydell even though he looked at me in his liquid-paper-toothed finery from the shadows of a little sideboard.

I grew rather uncomfortable and wondered if she was all right. She tried to smile and then said softly, 'It's my wedding anniversary today.'

'Really,' I said.

She smiled and still held my hand.

'He was a soldier. An American lad.'

I could see through her dark glasses that her eyes were closed.

I stood. She stood. She held my hand.

'He was so lovely. He had the kindest eyes.' She stopped and then let out a little sigh.

She let go of my hand and waddled into the kitchen. I could hear water pouring. She came back with a glass of orange cordial. It was warm. She had some money in her hand.

She gave it to me and said, 'It's awful to be alone. But that, I suppose, is the way some lives just pan out. He was lovely.'

She turned away and walked up the little steps to her house.

'You're a good worker all right,' she whispered.

I didn't drink the cordial and I didn't throw it away as I usually did. I walked to where some roses had finally started to grow and broke a stem off and plonked the rose in the glass of cordial.

At the door of Mrs Glazier's house I called out that I had something she might like. Bobby Rydell was singing.

I said that I would leave the glass on the step. She'd see the rose then. I looked at the money and thought that perhaps I should leave that too.

But then any money was handy because things were afoot. We had a school trip to the Snowy Mountains and a bit of extra cash would come in handy because Hairy Eric had made his presence felt in the meat department.

I promised myself that I would bring something back for Mrs Glazier.

The two cricketing tribes had made up on Kerry Packer's terms and so he settled into his glory days of being the great cricket revolutionary and unlocking opportunities for players. That meant, in many cases, players outstaying their welcome and trying to create little enclaves of power and influence through celebrity and notoriety. Namely showboating.

Rick McCosker came back to open in a test and then never played another. He'd gone off and played for Packer's cricket rebels but he ended up on the country circuit, his place taken in the Australian team by the South African born Kepler Wessels. Wessels scored runs. McCosker was the bloke who came out in the Centenary Test with a face swollen like a watermelon. Nobody wanted to remember that now.

Least of all when we were heading for the snow. And to Canberra, the nation's capital. So it came to be that the first time I visited Parliament House was after a week on a bus. It was sort of fun but everybody was already dressed for the snow when we were in subtropical Queensland and things got very ripe.

One of the bus drivers brought his son, Grigor, who looked and behaved like the prison warden out of a Stephen King novel.

This was an educational school trip down from Queensland to the Snowy Mountains. And we saw quite a lot. Lots of dead sheep by the roadside, some big turbines, some snow, some more road kill, a place that made lots of clogs, and Parliament House.

At the place that made lots of clogs I bought something I thought Mrs Glazier would like. A bottle opener sticking out the toe of a little clog.

What clogs had to do with anything educational was a bit moot but one of the teachers filled me in.

'Some Dutchy came over to work on the Hydro scheme and when he finished on that he set up this place. It's educational.' I looked at the teacher and then around at the walls of clogs.

'You can learn a lot about Holland...' the teacher said. 'And clogs. Things are changing. And he does all right. Taking the most of an opportunity that presents itself.'

We were supposed to meet our local member, a large jolly chemist called Big John. My parents never voted for him as he was a Liberal, but they liked him all the same for he was large and jolly. And, besides, the man he ran against was a man with a beard. A GI Joe type of beard.

As far as my father was concerned Big John's seat was safe – even though right up until the last week of the election campaign it looked like Bill Hayden might lead Labor to victory. But the last few days before the poll opened Mal Fraser's Liberal Party created a handy myth that Labor would impose a new wealth tax on the sacred cow of Australian life, the family home.

It was, as my father and most commentators pointed out, complete and utter bullshit. But it was good politics. Maybe it didn't sway that many votes, maybe it did, and maybe it was just Malcolm Fraser taking advantage of an opportunity that presented itself. Either way, he squeezed back into power and said the same things he always seemed to say and then disappeared as was his wont into the rooms of the Windsor Hotel.

That was all a month away and for now all we wanted was Big John.

But Big John the jolly chemist couldn't meet with us for he had politician work to pursue. In his place was an immense tray of sandwiches. After a week on a bus we were slightly demented and to say that the tray was attacked was an understatement. A girl I was in love with went at it hardest. She ate like some mad raptor. Seeing her at work on a rather angry looking beef sandwich I remembered how her mother's arms would wobble whilst on tuck-shop duty. I put this out of my head and stole furtive looks as she burped her way around the parliament on a guided tour.

To my distress Grigor the prison guard was being very solicitous and even gave her a tissue. I thought this was to wipe her face but as we walked across Kings Hall I saw that he was offering her a Big John sandwich.

At the end, as we stood by the doors of Parliament House, she staggered down the steps and upended herself and the contents of her stomach across the lawn. Democracy can be a heady thing.

I looked down at the Aboriginal Tent Embassy as the girl I loved hurled on the grass. A teacher told us why he thought Indigenous people felt they must protest. Most of us pretended to listen and then the teacher said he wished they didn't have to protest, but at least it was sort of good that they could. The War Memorial loomed in the distance.

That morning we had walked up and down the War Memorial's marbled floors and barely looked at the names etched into the walls. When we left I had looked back towards the great building. It loomed. That was the word for it, and it seemed to say something about possessing the landscape. It dominated the horizon. Yet the Tent Embassy was to me just as compelling. I didn't quite know why but both seemed to haunt me.

When we returned home I eventually got round to unpacking and I came across the clog with a bottle opener in the toe. I picked it up and wandered over to Mrs Glazier's house.

The lawn had been mowed.

I stood at the back door and looked at the step.

The glass of cordial was still there, as was the rose. Or what was left of it. Some petals were strewn either side.

A little spider web clung from the stem to the side of the step.

A horn beeped. I looked up to see my father waving.

'The old dear's gone to live up the coast with her son. Had a bit of a turn... Should be right but she won't be back here.'

For some stupid reason I said, 'Maybe it was the sugar in the sweet potato mash.'

My father didn't say anything. He just shook his head and went about his business.

I looked down at the clog bottle opener. It wasn't much of a present.

'What would Rick McCosker do?' I said to myself. Then I walked home to finish unpacking.

# 4

I had met 'The Dog' earlier in the evening at the front bar of the Criterion Hotel, a beautiful chalk-white pub on the banks of the gravy-stained Fitzroy River, over a sip or two. He was an engineering student and I was supposed to be a humanities one, and although it was an unlikely pairing of faculties we were happily sitting together in the brotherhood of the glass. We were drinking depth charges, shot glasses of bourbon sitting on the bottom of a pot of beer. You up-ended the pot and drained the beer, and the shot glass would slide down towards your gaping mouth.

The Dog wore a large cowboy hat.

'Nice hat,' I said.

''Tis. Belongs to my uncle Royce.'

'Oh.'

'Left it in the ute.'

'Yes.'

'Yes, thought I'd put it on.'

'Looks good.'

'Well I wouldn't know,' said The Dog. 'I've never wore it before, and I probably never will again.'

He drank and looked at me sideways.

'I'm not a cowboy.'

'Really?'

'Yes. Know it's hard to tell.'

We both wore T-shirts, football shorts and thongs.

'It's all about the hat,' I said.

'That,' said The Dog, 'and my lack of spurs.'

I nodded and we drank a bit more. It was TEAS day, Tertiary Education Assistance Scheme day, and thanks to the government some money had arrived in our accounts so we were assisting ourselves on a pleasant Thursday evening to the contents of a pleasant Central Queensland bar. If such a thing actually existed, that's where we were.

On the television in the corner of the bar, the newly minted Leader of the Labor Party, Bob Hawke, was crow-calling his way through a speech about bringing Australia together. It was another election and reconciliation was in the air.

Reconciliation meant, back then, bringing the vast collection of ordinary, everyday Australians together.

There weren't too many Indigenous ideas of reconciliation, it was more an idea of employees and employers, city and country, according to Bob.

The barmaid approached us. She liked Bob Hawke.

'Another round?'

The Dog and I took our time in deciding. The barmaid looked up at the television.

'Good old Hawkie, he'll sort it out.'

'What?' I said.

'The whole lot. What do you want?'

Bob started talking about the Franklin River and the need to protect the environment. Images of people chained to bulldozers and walking the streets of Hobart with placards led by a young general practitioner called Bob Brown.

'Like him too that bloke. Be a good catch. He's a doctor.'

Bob Brown stared back at an interviewer with his hair tousled and his anorak open and he smiled his crooked outdoorsman's smile.

'My sister's down there in Tasmania. Saving the creek,' said The Dog.

'Is your uncle Royce there too?'

'No, not Uncle Royce,' chuckled The Dog. 'Just my sister.'

The Dog's sister, like a lot of other people around our age, was trying to save the Franklin River from being dammed by the state Hydro-Electric Commission in Tasmania.

'She one of those greenies, those hippies? Those hairy types your sister?' said the barmaid, who had violently permed blonde hair tied with a large pink scrunchie.

'She is quite hairy,' nodded The Dog, 'but I don't know whether she's a hippie.'

'Them people are fuckin' communists,' said a huge man who did look like a cowboy.

'Oh no,' said The Dog. 'I think she just cares.'

The barmaid stared at us and the big cowboy burped.

'You right? You done?'

'We're done,' said The Dog. 'Come on, Uncle Royce left something else in the ute I can use.'

The Dog and I passed the television on our way out. Bob Hawke in his shiny suit and wavy hair was talking about, of all things, starting a kibbutz-style series of developments for young Australians to work together. I turned and looked back at the barmaid, with her permed hair and pink scrunchie, wiping down the bar, her eyes turned to the television and the two Bobs.

About thirty minutes later I crouched amid some bushes on the Bruce Highway and watched as The Dog gathered the 'something else' that Uncle Royce had left in the ute.

The Dog raised a shotgun and placed it near two large concrete testicles belonging to a huge statue of a Brahman bull, which stood as a monument to the Central Queensland beef industry.

'Bit of a pastime around here,' said The Dog. 'Thought we might as well join in.'

The Dog pulled the trigger and for a brief moment before the testicles shattered and left a sad little stab of steel reinforcing where the bullhood used to dangle, I thought that while people like The Dog's hairy sister were saving the environment and Bob Hawke wanted to bring Australia together, I was blowing the balls off a bull in the middle of Queensland on a Thursday night.

'Oh well, that was that,' muttered The Dog.

Indeed.

Bob Hawke spoke about reconciliation and a kibuttz and a year later he was on the Logies. Bob Brown was a *Cleo* bachelor of the year. And the balls on the Bruce Highway bull would be blown off again.

That was that in the 1980s.

•

A few months earlier I had finished watching *Gone with the Wind* in Brisbane. It was about the fortieth time I had seen it as an usher and while at first it was fun listening to the old women chortle over Clark Gable there were too many taps on the shoulder about mortality.

'Oh, here he is.'

'Isn't he lovely?'

'Hmmmm, well he's just digging up worms now.'

And they would all chuckle amongst themselves.

Armed with this realist's view of the make-believe Civil War drama and an awareness of the passing of time, I went to meet my friend Peter for lunch in the Brisbane mall.

In the middle of the mall we noticed a tall man with a long red face. His pants were hitched high. He had been wearing a suit but had shed the jacket and was standing in a little clump shaking hands with people. He stood the way Jehovah's Witnesses stand before they go off, bible and pamphlets in hand, to do their witnessing. A little nervously, perhaps aware that they are out of place.

And, in a way, the man and the group were there to try to grab some converts. For Malcolm Fraser was on the stump. Here in Queen Street Mall was the leader of our nation. Here was a politician in election mode. Here was a man who looked like he had been made-up as one of the suffering Confederate soldiers from Atlanta. Quite frankly, he looked awful. Vivien Leigh should have been saying 'Fiddle-dee-dee' to him and dabbing his swollen forehead with a wet towel.

Mal looked mournfully unhealthy, like he wasn't far from joining Clark Gable in digging up worms.

I looked at him. This was the man who was so reviled by so many. The man who had turfed out Whitlam. The man whose Razor Gangs were cutting government spending. The man whose government had imposed a wages freeze but had been racked with suggestions of scandal about 'bottom of the harbour' tax dodge schemes.

Here was the man whose government had delivered the unheard of whammy of double-digit unemployment and inflation.

Here he was trying to find a hand to shake. It wasn't that there were crowds railing at him or jeering. People were just walking past going about their usual business. I should have thought then that perhaps he wasn't so reviled. That perhaps lots of these people in one of the biggest cities in Australia voted for him.

He was just some awkward-looking bloke with a bright red face. He was the man about whom my father had said, 'This poor bugger must have run over a Chinaman's dog. Got no bloody luck.'

It was true. Ever since he had called the election nothing had really gone his way. The drought, which was so serious that it was given a capital D by the newspapers, had grown worse still. Fraser called the election thinking the leader of the opposition was to have been the watery Bill Hayden, he of the wet lips. Instead after months of agitation, Hayden fell on his sword and resigned for the good of the party he had served for so long and was replaced by the popular Bob Hawke.

My father liked Hayden but knew Hawke was the better bet.

'All that bloody work Bill did, and Old Runty will get all the pats on the back.' Then he laughed. 'Poor old Mal Fraser, it's a bit like choosing to bat when you think Freddie Titmus is bowling and then when you face up you see Jeff Thomson running in. He'll get creamed.'

At a fundraising campaign launch for Big John the jolly chemist, a journalist asked Tamie Fraser if she found Bob Hawke sexy. Nobody could quite believe that she even answered the question, least of all Mal Fraser.

She said yes, but then added that being sexy wasn't all that being a good prime minister was about.

Big John didn't look so jolly in the backyard of his house where the launch was held. One can only imagine what Malcolm thought. His wife didn't even rate him.

'Jesus she's just said he's a dud root! We've got it in the bag!' laughed Reg O'Brien, my dad's mate, in delight.

And now Fraser found himself in the Queen Street Mall on a horribly hot day looking like a dying extra from *Gone with the Wind*.

For no other reason, save for the fact that he was near, I yelled out the cry that had echoed at all the student demonstrations about Fraser's cuts to the education systems courtesy of his Razor Gang.

'One more cut – Fraser's throat!'

It bounced around the mall and Mal looked up. There was no anger or belligerence in his gaze. Just tiredness. My friend and I laughed and he bobbed his head and went back to his witnessing.

'What a bastard of a thing to do to a man,' said my father when I told him what I had shouted out to our leader.

I stared at my father and he stared back at me.

'You've got no bloody idea why you did that, do you?'

I stared back.

'No, I just shouted it out.' I couldn't quite understand why my father, a lifelong Labor man, was standing up for Malcolm Fraser.

'Jesus wept. Look, here's a man who at least stands up to get his head kicked. He may be some barge-arsed bastard but he's had a go. You, you pie-can. You don't even know why you yell out. Got no reason to yell out save for the fact you think it's funny.'

I shrugged my shoulders and said yeah.

'It's not a game of football! Christ, good people died so you could vote. Think of that next time you want a bit of a laugh. Please, son, don't take it for granted…' he softened a bit and then changed his tone. 'You know you could always get involved a bit more.'

I nodded a little too noncommittedly and he shook his head and sighed.

I said I would try to become involved. In a way, I did when I returned to my studies. It was just by chance, after a few after-class drinks with The Dog and a biology student called Karl, that I saw a banner outside a hall in town announcing a National Party anti-socialist rally was to be held that night and the special guest speaker was none other than the Deputy Prime Minister of Australia, Doug Anthony.

I should step in, I told myself, and see what it was that I did or didn't like. I should involve myself in seeing first-hand what it was that the conservatives had to offer me. It was also a chance to use the hall's toilets as I was busting.

I walked in and found the hall half full, if that. And I was the youngest person there save for a tall, thin teenager with the reddest hair I have ever seen. He wore a check shirt and blue jeans. And possessed the bluest and blankest eyes in the Southern Hemisphere. I noted this because he sat and stared at me after I had gratefully used the hall's dunny.

At first I thought he may well be a Duelling Banjo candidate, and he did in a vague way resemble a character from an early Wes Craven film. No, I told myself, he was just a bored kid who would rather be off watching telly... Or torturing waylaid tourists. No, watching telly, of course.

I busied myself with some of the literature that was given to each person as they entered the hall. A welcome to the Great Central Queensland Anti-Socialist Rally.

There was a photo of Doug Anthony. Anthony was a pleasant enough man and a tough as goats' knees politician who liked to holiday in a caravan on the north coast of New South Wales, but he had an unfortunate appearance when his lips and nose curled together. The time when he had his photo taken for the pamphlet was one of those occasions.

It was as if he had just smelt something unpleasant. I looked at his photo and then looked up to the table set out before us. Behind it sat Doug Anthony. He had the same expression.

Then I noticed that the check shirt had moved another row towards me. Still staring with those unblinking blue eyes crowned by that hair, which looked like the red fibre fillings in hard, bristly mattresses you found in bad flats or boarding houses.

He kept moving closer every time I looked away. I thought I must be imagining it. I looked at Doug and his half smile and then looked back. Sure enough the check shirt and the mattress hair had moved closer. He *was* a character from a Wes Craven film. I began to get slightly nervous. But, to my relief, he stopped looking at me when a woman of about fifty sat next to me. She had hurried in, collected her bits of paper and moved towards where I sat. I was so relieved I stood and welcomed her. She was slightly taken aback but then returned the warmth of my panicked hello.

'I'm so glad I didn't miss Doug speak,' she said.

'Yes, yes,' I said looking at her and then to mattress hair. He had turned back to look at us.

'I just had to finish a game of badminton and hotfoot it down here...without a shower!' she giggled. 'But it's worth sitting in your sweat to hear Doug speak.'

I nodded and shot my eyes to where the check shirt was. He was on the move again. No longer looking at me, but moving.

I thought of heading for the door but then a small man with a neat beard and smooth voice stood and asked us to sing the national anthem. We all sang 'God Save the Queen'.

The MC had the bland pleasantness of an afternoon radio presenter reading out song dedications to people in hospitals. He started by giving astounding facts about what the Labor Party would do if they got into power. They would destroy the gains made and return all wealth to the union bosses and their mates in the city.

'Think 'bout that,' whispered the MC-cum-DJ.

I thought about it and all I could come up with was double-digit unemployment and inflation.

He quoted some astonishingly unflattering figures about the number of working hours lost through industrial action, paused and whispered again, 'Think 'bout that.'

He sounded as if he were introducing an Andy Williams record for somebody who was waiting to have their gallstones out.

'How many ministers were forced to resign in disgrace? Here is the "Hawaiian Wedding Song" for Dudley in the Rockhampton Base Hospital... Yes, think 'bout that.'

It was slightly surreal, and with every patient dedication and prophecy of doom, mattress hair would move closer. He had, in fact, moved to our row. He looked down at me and he seemed to crouch as if ready to leap. I looked at him and balled my fists. The smooth voice invited to the stage a great son of the National Party... Doug...

There was an inexplicably long pause before 'Anthony' and during this time mattress hair leapt up and sprang towards me.

I shot up and the woman who was sitting in her sweat looked up with her mouth open.

Mattress hair shot towards me and whispered in the breaking voice of a shy adolescent, 'Sorry sir, I'm sorry, I have to go to the toilet. Excuse me.'

I had begun to yell.

'Anthony,' said the smooth voice. There was a silence as my shout rolled around the room.

'Oh yes,' sighed the woman next to me.

Some people stared at the mattress head as he stumbled past to the toilet and then to me.

My yell became an attempted cheer and I applauded. I sounded slightly deranged but I suppose I must have fitted in because the woman sitting in her sweat now stood in it and applauded too. Soon the forty or so others present followed.

Doug Anthony took to the stage a little taken aback but nonetheless happy enough.

He had a speaking style that suited his appearance, sounding as if he were trying to suppress a yawn.

I sat back down and my neighbour smiled at me, nodding. 'You like him too. You like Doug.'

I tried to nod and smile but I felt a little unhinged and settled for trying to look like I was listening for the wisdom of Doug.

Somehow Doug lost me. I think he lost everybody. He must have been tired. Maybe it was because he was in Rockhampton and it was a safe Labor seat. At least he was having a go.

He welcomed us all and thanked us for the warm, 'the very warm' welcome with a nod to us at the back of the room.

Then he started talking about the socialist menace of Bob Hawke and the unions. Of how Labor couldn't be trusted with the economy and the defence of Australia.

'Because...deeeeefence...is...ve-reeeey...important.'

There were a few 'Hear, hears' and the odd cough, and Doug Anthony stared out at us: the Great Central Queensland Anti-Socialist Rally.

He took a great sigh and then said something to fill the space I guess.

'Socialists all over the world have undermined and destroyed some wonderful countries...some fine economies...'

He paused and seemed to search for some nation.

'Some lovely countries...you only have to look at Argentina to see that.'

I leant forward and looked around. Nobody moved, save for the coughers and the hear-hearers.

'He can't say that,' I muttered.

'What?' said the woman next to me.

'Well, how can he say that? About Argentina.'

'What?'

'Well, they're a right-wing government, a military junta.' I looked at her.

She stared at me a little and then, as the room applauded in response to Doug's mentioning the need to protect beef interests, she said quickly, 'Yes...yes...yes...well they are so far right that they are... LEFT!' She applauded loudly.

'He's so good Doug, isn't he?'

I was worried about the kid in the check shirt with the mattress hair. He came back from the toilet and sat at the end of our row. I thought that maybe the woman sitting in her sweat had some sort of point. As soon as I thought that, I knew I should go.

I stood and applauded and inched myself away. The woman only had eyes for Doug.

And Doug was looking happy that his speech was done. He nodded and raised a hand.

I waved back and he raised his hand again.

As I walked out I saw a man leaning in the doorway. He was smoking a roll-your-own cigarette and had pushed his hat back on his head. I had seen that hat before. It was a cowboy hat. I'd seen it hunched down over a shotgun as I crouched near some ceramic testicles.

I stared at it a little too long for he looked at me and nodded. So I nodded back.

'Are you Royce?' I said.

He nodded.

I nodded.

He looked at me.

'I'm a friend of your nephew's... I think.'

'Kieran?' he said slowly.

Kieran was The Dog's name.

'And you're here tonight?'

I looked back.

A great hand took mine with a shake that rattled my shoulder bone.

'Well at last he's making some good mates.'

Uncle Royce was delighted that one of The Dog's 'cobbers' had taken the time to turn up to the rally.

'S'portant that you young bucks have a look-see at what's going on round the traps,' said Uncle Royce.

He spoke in a well-rounded voice and seemed to have a habit of dropping the beginnings and endings off words to the extent that he sounded like he was doing a Huntin' and Fishin' character from some murder weekend, or was an old radio actor. The more he talked, the more he sounded like Ray Warren, the football and racing caller from the old KB Cup mid-week comp who had been blaring away on the new Sky racing channel in the pubs.

I nodded. I thought I should say something.

'It was good.'

Uncle Royce nodded back and took a drag on his fag. I noticed one of his eyes was turned away from the other. He blew smoke out from his nose.

'Oh yes, fine speaker...is Doug...did well. But they're up a canin' times up this round I'm afraid. Our little mate Bob'll get the nod.'

I looked over at Doug Anthony answering some journalists' questions. He did look a little tired and I wondered what would provoke a person to do such things to themselves. I mean, how many anti-socialist rallies does a man have in him? He still had to say hello to some of the more ardent anti-socialists, including the woman who sat in her sweat.

Uncle Royce flicked away his smoke and rearranged my arm with another firm handshake. 'Be bound to cross paths, good to meet you 'n' say hello to that nephew of mine.'

The next time I was sharing a drink with The Dog he shook his head.

'What did you do to Uncle Royce?'

I looked back at him.

'He likes you. Shit, he says he wants to go fishing with you sometime.'

'Is that a good thing?'

The Dog shrugged his shoulders.

'What's wrong with his eye?'

'A horse kicked him in the head. I think you could say it knocked him stupid.'

'Right.'

'Willy... He's got daughters.' The Dog sipped his drink and raised his eyebrows.

The election did seem to be slipping away from the Liberals. Whether Malcolm Fraser had run over a Chinaman's dog and luck was against him, or whether it was the end of the conservative parties 'go', there didn't seem to be much opposition to Bob Hawke. For it was Hawke and not so much Labor who was fighting the campaign. Great advertisements of smiling Bob, with that hair of his that looked like it came out of a show bag, peered out from the television and from newspapers.

The Labor Party was a postage stamp on this particular envelope. Indeed, Bob was an altogether different package.

It wasn't as if he was unknown for he had already became a minor folk hero with his lad-about-town and Mr Fix-It persona.

But he sounded so different from other politicians. Fraser spoke in that peculiar aching accent and Gough Whitlam had sounded fruity and well-versed in the ways of the ancients.

But Bob Hawke seemed to have a heightened voice that represented the suburbs. And that was his key. He was such a recognisable suburban type. The boy made good. The nifty, confident little bloke at the local sporting club who had a go at footy but was very good at cricket.

He embraced the stuff of the common man, but wore it with the style of a lad done well. He loved a punt and didn't look out of place in the members, but he would always be welcome on the flat.

He'd given away the grog, following the example of his great hero John Curtin, to pursue the highest political office, but unlike Curtin's quiet commitment to Caucus Hawke's was splashed across the media.

His dramas were well known and his emotional volatility was a suburban soap played out for the nation. He was a star.

No other political figure had embraced the common pursuits of Australia like Hawke. Yes, Holt had liked swimming in the surf but that was at the knob-end of the wealthy beachside retreats of Victoria and he went and drowned himself. Menzies had adored cricket but only from a comfy chair with a cigar. Fraser just seemed to be all at sea with sport and everybody else. And nobody could ever imagine Hawke being booed at a football match like Whitlam.

Hawke was a lad made good who had a foot in both Australias. He was admired in the leafier suburbs as a Rhodes scholar but while he was in England he played cricket for his university and at the same time also held the world beer-drinking record for a yard glass.

His ascent was also at a time when Australian popular culture had just spent a decade of self-referencing and imagining the idea of Australians and Australianness, especially through its cinema. An Australian voice was being heard for the first time in a long time, a voice that was having a holiday from pretending to be a mix between British or American. So it was a heightened form of Australianness that enabled him to appeal to so many.

In many respects he sounded more modern, immediate and recognisable than the squatter-like, hungry bummed Fraser.

Though the idea of Hawke as sexy and alluring to women was passed around, quite frankly it was considered a bit of a joke. Even though Doug Anthony had the ability to command the sweaty woman from badminton, politicians were a pretty dismissible lot.

'Oh Christ, I can't imagine any of them doing it,' said a friend. 'But I suppose he seems the most normal of them.' She winced a little. 'No, no. No. It doesn't do any good to think of political leaders being on the job. It's hard enough putting up with them as it is.'

I asked my mum what she thought of Bob after poor Tamie Fraser's bit of foot-in-mouth regarding his appeal.

'Oh good God, him and his cackle...it'd be like a bit of slap and tickle with a rooster.'

My aunty Rita was even more dismissive. 'No, thank you. He's too much like an old kelpie, all dick and bone. Like mine with a bit more meat.'

It was almost as if the whole election was like a sideshow alley. Hawke was a little bit old-fashioned, somebody who used to be a likely lad but really was older than Malcolm Fraser. He should know better. Perhaps he liked to imagine himself as a cross between the Jack Thompson unionist in *Sunday Too Far Away* and Alvin Purple, the suburban sex god, with a little bit of the white-shoe brigade thrown in for good measure.

To the old lady who owned the milk bar on the corner he was, 'A dirty sex-mad bastard.' Then she would add with a wink, 'He's got my vote.'

Then somebody in the Liberal Party or some advertising agency had an idea about how Malcolm Fraser could combat the allure of Bob Hawke. It was an idea that left policies and even old-style fear campaigns in the out-tray and was supposed to be about capturing the strengths of Fraser. In an awkwardly long television ad.

In the house I shared with two mechanics, Mal and Stevo, the advertisement never failed to elicit a response.

Mal's real name was Darren, but because his diet consisted of Cornish pasties, hot chips and lime-flavoured milk Darren became known as Mal, as in malnutrition. He smoked Winfield Blues and the odd bong or two, and would laugh with a bark.

Stevo was a long-haired, long-armed ladies' man who was forever asking where the book he was reading was. The book would invariably be a magazine dealing with mufflers or exhaust or motorbikes. He was a purist as a mechanic – 'a mechanic's mechanic' according to Mal.

We sat around the living room on beanbags as Mal pulled on a bong.

'Bill,' Stevo said languidly. 'Bill, you seen that book I was reading?'

'No, mate.'

'What do AUSTRALIANS think about leadership?' said a voice that sounded like Malcolm Fraser's cousin.

Mal exhaled and said softly, 'Bullshit.'

Stevo and I looked at the television.

John Newcombe was on an ad spruiking for Malcolm Fraser. He was saying something about Fraser's commitment to the youth of Australia being shown by the Fraser government's support of tennis coaching in Australia.

'Yeah. Grow up, play tennis and drink Cinzano.'

'Must be the drink for today,' said Stevo mimicking the Newk's catchcry from the Cinzano aperitif ad.

'If he's such a fucking hero why doesn't he flog Fourex?' said Mal. 'He can't beat those Swedish guys anyway.'

'Where's my book, boys?'

'Oh bullshit!' Mal pointed to the screen.

Peter Brock and Alan Jones, motoring champions, spoke like cardboard puppets about how you couldn't trust an untested driver with a motor that was known to blow.

'What would a fuckin' Holden man know,' mumbled Mal.

'Strong words, Mal,' I said.

'Wish he knew where my book was.'

'Oh piss off, Herman,' said Mal to Malcolm Fraser.

'Herman Munster,' Stevo said. 'Herman Munster.'

Mal barked a bit. 'Shit that was a good show. That car was great, that hot rod the Munsters tooled around in.' He enjoyed a bit more reverie, then took a bite out of a pastie and held up his lime-flavoured milk, 'Must be the drink of today. Piss off, Herman.' Mal threw a packet of fags at Malcolm/Herman.

'If I vote for Hawkie, will he find my book?' asked Stevo.

'Too right he will, he's Hawkie. Must be the drink of today,' Mal said. Then he farted.

Somebody had had the bright idea to get a collection of champion sports people to give testimonials about Malcolm Fraser. Daring stuff. Bob Hawke is a sporty bloke, we'll get household sporting champions and we'll meet Hawke's appeal head-on by having these champs say why Mal should get the people's vote. It didn't work because it didn't make sense. Nobody thought that any of those guys were going to be worse off or would really care if Fraser didn't win.

But what that ad did do was form a bridge between sport and politics, a clumsy one to be sure, but one that would be crossed very energetically a few months later. And Australia would change. But first there was the election to be won.


On the afternoon of 5 March 1983 I got a phone call just as I was heading off to vote. I had been heading off for quite some time. I had spent the afternoon with Mal sitting under the Hills hoist.

He had devised a drinking game. He called it Moselle Roulette.

We sat on plastic chairs directly opposite each other. On the end of one of the arms of the Hills hoist we hung a cask of wine.

Both Mal and I had a glass. We would swing the Hills hoist around and if the arm that was loaded stopped above either one of us we would pour a glass and drink the wine.

Neither of us spoke much. We sat listening to a Mental as Anything album on loop: 'The Nips are Getting Bigger'. Sometimes we hummed along but mostly we busied ourselves with wasting a Saturday. Sometimes I thought of my father handing out how-to-vote cards. Then another song played and another twirl of the Hills hoist went round.

It was a phone call that finally got me away from the Hills hoist. It was The Dog.

'Could you,' he said, 'be a mate and do me a favour?'

'Sure,' I told him.

He was going on a date.

'Good for you,' I said.

'Thanks, mate,' he said.

Now here was the thing, according to The Dog. He had himself a date and he was off to a party.

There was a pause. I picked up a paper and wondered when the pause would stop or if it would build into a silence.

It built into a silence.

'Look, mate,' said The Dog.

'What do you want?' I asked.

'Can you go on a date...with a girl...who is the flatmate of the girl I am going on a date with...mate?'

'You're a poet, Dog,' I said.

'No, I'm desperate,' said The Dog.

'Jesus you've talked it up.'

It wouldn't be long, he said, just an hour or two. Then I could nick off back to whatever party I was going to go to.

After a while I said all right because I couldn't think of what party I wanted to go to. I didn't think I was in a fit state to nick off to any party. But I still said all right.

The Dog breathed a long sigh down the phone line.

'Thanks, mate. Can you pop around at about six-thirty?'

Before he hung up, I asked, 'What's her name?'

'Oh, it's Rita...mate.'

Rita. The name of my aunt. I closed the paper and went to vote and go on a blind, literally, date.

I called out to Mal that I was off on a date and he mumbled something about me taking his lucky shirt.

'Never know, Bill, could come in handy.'

I gratefully accepted his offer and, undeterred that Mal was about half my size, I marched off in a body shirt printed with hang-gliders.

Rita was a quiet girl. Which was just as well because there wasn't anything much anyone could say. There was something familiar about her, and although I couldn't quite put my finger on it, I certainly put my foot in my mouth by mentioning as an icebreaker that I was wearing my mate's lucky shirt. Several times.

The Dog looked resigned more than anything else and shrugged his shoulders to his companion for the night.

'I didn't know he was going to be shit-faced,' he said nonchalantly.

We ate spaghetti, I think, and quite a lot of garlic bread. I tried to make small conversation as best I could. Unfortunately it was at the wrong table for I had gone to the toilet and had forgotten where our table was. I lurched back and helped myself to some more garlic bread.

We sat in silence. I attempted to break it. Forget the shirt. Think election.

'Do you…' I paused, trying to think of what to say.

'Do *you*…do you think Bob Hawke is…sexy?' Even I winced. The shirt would have been better.

The Dog blanched and his partner kicked him and looked at him through narrowed eyes.

'Well we should be going, Keiran,' said The Dog's companion.

The Dog nodded as he stood above me, then he lent down, 'Thanks, mate. Please be nice, she's my cousin.'

'Royce's daughter?'

He nodded and said goodbye. When he was gone I turned to Rita.

'So you're Royce's daughter?' I smiled.

She stared at me. She didn't really do anything but she didn't look happy. She was a girl on a blind nightmare. I tried to break the ice again.

'This is a lucky shirt,' I said. 'We're going to have good luck.'

She said nothing.

'Anything you want to do?'

She said nothing.

I felt, I must admit, a little ashamed all of a sudden.

'Anything at all?' I said as nobly as I could.

She suddenly smiled.

I looked at her.

I tried to smile.

'I would like to stick this fork in your stupid fucking face.'

She stood up, started crying and walked off.

I waited for a moment, took another piece of garlic bread, then got the guilts and went after her. I called out her name and winced because I sounded strangely like my father.

Rita had walked across the road and was sitting on a bench.

An arm grabbed me from a hole in the wall at the front of the restaurant and told me I hadn't paid. It was like something out of a bad video clip, or if I had paid more attention to the film elective I had chosen at university I might have been able to say it was a homage to Jean Cocteau's *Beauty and the Beast*. It was, after all, a surrealistic romance. It had all the trappings of election night for me.

I couldn't see anything else except the arm, so I apologised to its hairy pit and made good my bill.

By the time I made my way over to where Rita sat she was crying.

I stood for a while and, when she had stopped crying, she told me to piss off. Then she started crying again and I waited, eating my garlic bread. When she stopped again she told me to fuck off.

'Come on,' I said, 'the shirt isn't that bad.'

This time when she looked at me she laughed.

'There, you see, it is lucky.'

She laughed a little more.

I sat down and for a little while we said nothing. Then she told me that her father, Royce, was very happy when she had told him she was gong on a blind date. When I asked her why she had told her father she was going on a blind date she said it was to make him happy. I suggested that Royce should come on the date too if dates made him happy.

She looked at me. 'I only told him because…he wants to hear stuff like that.'

Rita, it turned out, was gay. She had a partner who worked, of all things, for a conservative political party. I thought of the anti-socialist rally and I shuddered.

'She doesn't play badminton, does she?'

Rita looked a bit nonplussed and I carried on.

'Well, that would make your old man happy at least,' I said with another attempt at flattery.

She looked away and wiped her eyes. 'I love my father very much,' she said slowly.

I told her I loved mine. And I told her that sometimes, when I thought about it, I felt I let him down. Especially when I was wearing a body shirt two sizes too small.

Rita asked me if I was as nice as this when I was sober.

I thought of my old man again and knew all he ever really wanted was for the people he cared about to tell him the stuff that mattered.

'I reckon, Rita, that if people could be straight with people they care about then it works both ways.'

She laughed and told me to shut up.

We didn't say much for a long time. Then she said, 'You asked me if there was anything I wanted to do.'

I nodded.

'I've always wanted to climb that tree.' She pointed to a great bare hoop pine in a dark park nearby.

'Let's go,' I said.

So on election night me and a quiet girl who loved her father very much and didn't want to hurt him started climbing the great dying needles of an old tree. It seemed immense, especially after an afternoon of Moselle Roulette.

We climbed quite high. I looked up and the stars seemed close. We stayed for a little while. Rita laughed and whooped a bit and then said, more to herself than to me, 'I'm going to tell him.'

Then we started to climb down. I led the way. I don't know why, I was fairly wobbly and kept missing branches, and Rita was a far more adept night climber than me. I kept holding her up as her boots narrowly missed my groping fingers. I tried to tell her a couple of times to slow down but she was on a mission and I was out of breath so I don't think she really understood my wheezings. She finally stood on my hand.

Rita, like her father, was a rather hefty person. I howled and reached for her boot to move it.

Rita quickly removed her boot. 'Sorry,' she said.

I was left grasping nothing and fell away. I tried to say, 'You're right,' but it became a scream and then ... well, it was a miracle that the ground was so soft. I had fallen through the odd branch or two but that didn't seem to have had much effect.

I wheezed in a heap and turned over to see the stars above. It was fine after a while and I assured Rita that I was okay. 'It's a lucky shirt, you know.'

She hugged me and I hugged her. I walked home and she went off to her life.

Back at the house the television was on but the sound was turned down and I staggered in and collapsed on a beanbag. Malcolm Fraser was fighting back a tear. He looked relieved and a little embarrassed, like a guy who has finally admitted to something he's been denying for a long time. He seemed like he was going to cry. I suppose in his own way he'd fallen from a tree. Never mind. With a quiver of his lip he was gone.

Then Hawkie appeared and he waved with his wife Hazel by his side. His suit was very shiny, his hair very wavy and he was very happy.

He began his speech. I couldn't hear it, which was just as well because it seemed to go on and on and on.

From downstairs in the dark, there came a voice. It sounded like it came from under the Hills hoist.

'Must be the drink for today.' It was Mal's voice.

Then he started to sing 'The Nips are Getting Bigger' by Mental as Anything.

Mal may have sung but it looked for all the world like it came from Bob Hawke's mouth. It was a unique victory speech.

The Hawke government hit the ground running and conveniently found a four billion dollar hole in the budget that the Fraser government had forgotten to mention. Bob was aghast, and being the responsible managerial leader of a responsible managerial party, common sense and responsibility had to be maintained.

Basically it meant that all bets were off as far as election promises and commitments were concerned. And, in doing this, Hawke and his increasingly visible sidekick Paul Keating demarcated their government from the seemingly bacchanalian excesses of the previous Whitlam Labor administration. And Malcolm Fraser's mob.

Whitlam's crew had apparently been mad enthusiasts and inexperienced babes in the woods, while Fraser and his friends were portrayed as scheming, unimaginative and untrustworthy.

Bob and his boys would walk the straight and narrow, the good path of the middle ground. They would be economically responsible.

That didn't mean nothing happened. Something was always on with Bob about, but it was done Bob-style: businesslike and grey-suited.

At a national economic summit in Canberra, just three months after 'The Nips are Getting Bigger' victory speech, lots of knights of the business world – men with names like Sir Arvi and Sir Rodney and Sir Peter – along with a host of action men in double-breasted suits, broke bread with unionists. Old-fashioned unionists with their noses directed to all points of the compass and new models with their hard eyes and shiny suits, and political ambitions tucked away neatly.

My father was amazed to see a man with whom he had come to fisticuffs at a party meeting.

'Did you see him? That great melon-headed pie-can? A left-wing clown like him talking in parliament…' I thought that my old man was outraged, but then he let out a great pealing laugh.

'Son, it is a bloody marvel. Not too many places where old melon head could bang on with the bosses. Top shelf. Old Runty has done well.'

Old Runty was my father's name for Bob Hawke, and although my father didn't think that much of Hawke – 'What sort of bloke combs his hair that much? And what sort of fella does what he did to poor old Bill Hayden?' – even my father had to admit that for a while at least Hawke was the biggest name in town.

•

During Australia's winter months and into early spring something was happening on the other side of the world. Something that hadn't happened ever.

'Shit, Bill,' wheezed Mal as we sat under the Hills hoist. 'Bondy might do it!'

Bondy. One of our rich tubby blokes, Alan Bond, had spent his money wisely. Or maybe the Americans hadn't spent theirs well because Bond's yacht *Australia II* was proving highly competitive in the America's Cup.

In Mal's words, 'We're travelling well, we could win, we could win.'

And he took a swig of lime milk as he readied himself for another round of Moselle Roulette.

'Fair dinkum, we could win.'

The change in Mal's attitude was interesting. Only a month or so before we'd been having dinner in a pub. I had a fisherman's basket, which amounted to a few sprigs of parsley, some chips and lots of fried batter, while Mal went all out and ordered a chicken schnitzel that looked big enough to land a helicopter on.

Mal had smuggled in his usual lime milk while I tried to moderate with a shandy.

'I'm off for a slash,' I said with the age-old Australian male's declaration of intent.

'Might join you,' barked Mal.

On the way we heard a couple laughing about *Australia II*'s easy victories over the other contenders in the preliminary races that decided who would compete against the American boat. The yachts owned by those European counts, barons and newspaper magnates were no competition for Bondy's boat with the winged keel. The miracle device.

'Really. It's as if they own the friggin' boat themselves instead of some millionaire,' sniffed Mal.

We busied ourselves in the toilets and, as I stood at the trough, Mal continued to hold forth before entering a cubicle.

'He's got the balls to call his boat "Australia" like he fuckin' owns the country. Who cares about his stupid boat, 'snot like these fellas ever win – oh yes!'

I turned around. Mal was looking down with a sort of awe spreading across his face.

He turned to me and pointed into the cubicle.

'Now that...that there...that is something you don't see every day. Keep your fuckin' winged keels, *that* is a bit o' natural genius... Come here and look.'

He laughed and shook his head.

'What?' I said with trepidation.

'Come here. That is better than a winged keel. That's a bit o' art!'

A man with a long beard had joined us.

'Hard to believe that's been backed out of human being's arse,' he said. 'More like a gorilla's!'

'Mate, no gorilla could ever do that, that's what separates them from us!' Mal laughed.

In the bowl, a giant turd wound around itself and seemed to rear up. It was awe-inspiring enough if you were of a particular bent, but somebody, perhaps the person who had dropped it, had stuck two matches on top of the thing so it resembled some type of creature.

'You think it's that good?' said the hairy man. And he half smiled with an aura of proprietorship.

Mal pointed. 'You –'

The hairy man shook his head. 'No, no, mate. Not me. I couldn't do that.'

'You COULDN'T?' I almost shrieked. 'Mate, you should say you WOULDN'T. Why would you do that?'

The hairy man looked at me. 'Well, it's a bit like that Kiwi bloke...'

I stared at him. What did he mean? Some New Zealander had done this?

'That Hillary fella, maybe it was just there. Like Bondy having a crack at the Yanks.'

That is where Hairy lost Mal.

'Oh turn it up, mate. It's just a big turd in a toilet...appreciate it for what it's worth.'

I walked back to our table a bit stunned. I looked at my fisherman's basket and knew I wouldn't be touching it. I looked around the pub, it was half-price night so it was full. Maybe the owner/creator of the creature in the bowl was still there. I didn't know if any of them were New Zealanders. How could you tell?

I thought of Edmund Hillary. I felt embarrassed for Sir Ed and myself.

Mal sniffed, 'Silly goose, why would you go and ruin something you don't see every day by talking about that friggin' boat race?'

But that was then. Under the Hills hoist, Mal, like everybody else, was on board. Bondy had fought back to level the final series against the Americans. It had come down to one race.

Well, Bondy hadn't done it, the crew had I guess. The captain of the boat, John Bertrand, a guy with neat hair and a porn-star moustache, was responsible for the sailing. And Ben Lexcen, a journeyman designer, had the idea for the winged keel. Lexcen was a shaggy-haired bear of a man who wore glasses and looked as if he was the sort of person who would like to sing Seekers songs. Then there was blond-haired, white-toothed Warren Jones, the smooth super sporty spokesman for the Alan Bond *Australia II* syndicate.

But it was Bondy who was really running the race. He was head of the syndicate. Even though that name, 'the syndicate', had something vaguely sinister or shifty about it, everybody seemed to be getting swept up into the fervour of the America's Cup.

In more than a hundred years of races, nobody had ever beaten the Yanks to win the America's Cup and here was Bondy and his syndicate only one race away from victory.

Perhaps if we had had a better cricket team, or if we had won more gold medals at the Olympics and Commonwealth Games. Perhaps if there had been more tennis players holding up trophies and cups like the Australian champions did in the 1950s and 1960s. Perhaps then people wouldn't have hopped on board so much.

There was a long tradition of Australia taking part in the America's Cup races and it was an achievement of technical innovation and persistence that the syndicate had done so well.

But because Australia had had such a lean run of sporting success in recent years, the yacht races seemed to be taking on a greater significance. And people were going overboard. The hairy man and the creature of the bowl were a perfect example of the madness that was gripping people.

Little boxing kangaroo flags, like the one flown on *Australia II*, seemed to be sprouting everywhere. Even Mal had one stuck on his Falcon.

'Getting in to it are we, Mal?' I asked him.

He shrugged his shoulders and barked, 'Why not? Be good to give it to the Yanks, and besides the boss'll put on a bit of a piss-up if they win.'

Perhaps it was the promise of a national piss-up that was intoxicating the population. And of course there was always Bob Hawke.

The day that *Australia II* was competing in the deciding race of the America's Cup I was, as it happened, also on the water. The Dog's uncle Royce wanted to take his new boat out for a bit of a burl and I was invited along. The Dog, who had recently graduated and was on his way to a successful career in the mining industry, thought it might be nice to have a few drinks and a bit of a fish by way of saying goodbye.

It was a nice big, white boat with lots of shining bits of silver steel. Uncle Royce and his cowboy hat looked very proud and content. It was a lovely sunny day, with the promise of heat growing as the hours wore on. An Australian flag fluttered above Uncle Royce at the wheel and there was a rack of rods and a big esky.

'Be usin' that esky before too long, but we should wait to see how our boys are doin' in the Cup,' said Uncle Royce.

I looked at him and wondered if Rita had told him anything yet.

He seemed to be having a hoot, although I wasn't sure if his lairising at the helm was enthusiasm or simply a lack of assurance with his vessel.

'You're chewing up the brine there, Uncle Royce,' quipped The Dog as he gripped a shiny piece of steel with whitening knuckles.

'Just clearing the tubes and runnin' it in.'

The boat hit a wave at speed, groaned a bit and Uncle Royce's hat fell over his face. I grasped a piece of shiny steel as well and The Dog and I shared a look.

'Right then, there you have it,' said Uncle Royce and he half turned with his funny eye staring off into the distance.

The boat moaned a bit more. Uncle Royce did something with the levers and I was reminded of my father's mower controls. I grabbed the shiny steel with both hands.

We weren't sure if he meant to, but it seemed that Uncle Royce had decided to stop the boat there. He turned the radio up louder and started unwrapping a bit of material in clear plastic wrap.

The radio was tuned into the concluding moments of the America's Cup yacht race on the other side of the world and the commentator was getting louder so it was decided we should prepare for the approaching victory.

The commentator spoke about the finishing gun puffing a little explosion of white smoke to signal the end of the race and the end of America's domination of the America's Cup. Uncle Royce, The Dog and I all shook hands and cheered.

'Right, let's open that esky 'n' celebrate!' said our brave captain. 'I'll raise this!'

Uncle Royce flapped a boxing kangaroo flag.

The sounds of celebrations and hooting horns from Rhode Island echoed through the radio as The Dog and I stared into the esky.

Uncle Royce joined us and we stared in silence.

'Righto... Righto...' intoned Uncle Royce finally.

We continued to stare.

'Righto, I've buggered up a bit here. Obviously brought the wrong esky.'

Obviously. We looked down at a couple of old bags of pipis, little shellfish that are used for bait, and a half bottle of Cottee's lime cordial.

'Thought it was a bit light on. Bit of a bugger.'

Still, Uncle Royce was determined to toast the boys' success, for the commentator on the radio and all the DJs and callers that followed spoke of how historic this event was.

Suddenly it wasn't *Australia II*, the play thing of a rich man's syndicate, that won a race, it was Australia that had beaten the best in the world. We stood in the heat and poured warm cordial into three plastic cups.

What we swallowed tasted like some sort of awful medicine and we all grimaced as if we were bad actors playing hardened sea-dogs swigging on overproof rum. 'Christ, that's a drop to remember,' said Royce as he scoured his throat and spat into the sea.

There was no other liquid on board so it was thought, for safety's sake, best to pull the plug on the outing.

'Load up those rods, boys – least we might fish a bit before heading in,' was the cry from Uncle Royce.

By this time, Bob Hawke had crystallised the day's events. Draped in a champagne-sodden jacket emblazoned with flags and the word AUSTRALIA Bob Hawke had crackled into the ages, 'Any boss who sacks his workers today for not turning up is a bum!'

'Go, Bob,' muttered The Dog.

'Oh here he is on the act! Who's running the country while he has a party?'

That day marked the beginning of a definition of being unAustralian.

The prime minister didn't just send a message of congratulations. He was, it seemed, the chief cheerleader. And it was fun. He was one of us, joining in with the fun and cheers. Sport and national worth had come together as one, and the lover of all things sport, that old silver-haired suburban sports jock Bob Hawke, was the man to anoint the moment. He ensured that prime ministers ever after would be the Tom Joads of sporting victory.

Wherever there's a sporting success – I'll be there.

Wherever there's a sweaty back to slap – I'll be there.

Wherever there's a cup to hold aloft – I'll be there.

Australians, everyday ordinary Australians who Bob Hawke had hoped to reconcile with each other, were all people who thought this sort of event was what brought out the best in us.

I doubt Hawke set out with a deliberate intent to do this, it just happened – a combination of event and personality forming a heady cocktail of pleasant nationalistic boofheadedness.

But all of a sudden the boxing kangaroo took on a more patriotic and fervent meaning. The boxing kangaroo had a long history in Australia, it was used by Australian servicemen in the World War II, but this latest version was a bright, childlike effort that became symbolic of success. Suddenly it seemed we all liked waving flags, both national and the boxing kangaroo.

Amidst all the partying there were moments of attempted gravitas on the radio as experts, and even the PM, pointed out this was more than a sporting victory. It seemed more important because already there was talk of the economic boom that would come from hosting the Cup.

Sporting success meant economic viability. Australia's technical innovations had won the Cup as much as anything else and so it was victory for our research and development skills as much as our derring-do on the water.

We were better than the best.

As we listened to the radio we realised that the prawns and pipis had travelled along the highway of decay quite a way. When we tried to thread the hooks the bait dissolved in our fingers.

'They're off like Granny's tweeds. Sorry lads. We'll zip back and I'll shout you lunch.'

But the big nice white boat and its shiny bits of steel wouldn't be zipping anywhere, at least not today. Royce straightened his hat, pulled throttles and pressed a few buttons in a deliberate, unhurried manner.

The boat sounded like a coffee grinder on slow motion. We puttered back to whence we came at a snail's pace.

'Okay, seems I've cooked somethin' 'n the beast so we won't be breaking any records. But we'll get there.'

It wasn't unpleasant, but it was hot, and soon The Dog took the wheel and Uncle Royce popped himself down beside me.

'Marvellous effort.'

'Yeah, terrific.'

Someone on the radio said it was the greatest day in Australian history since federation. Uncle Royce smiled.

'Gettin' a little carried away but, you know... It's history we've lived through today.'

I felt sunburnt and thirsty, and smelt like dead prawns, so I nodded. I was living through history.

For the umpteenth time, highlights from the Cup campaign were played over the radio to celebrate the victory. Dreams. It seemed it was all about following your dreams and holding onto them until you achieve them.

Uncle Royce tilted his head back and closed his eyes. He seemed lost in thought.

Nobody spoke and the coffee-grinder beat of the engine churned on.

'Dreams. Tricky things,' muttered Royce, his eyes still closed.

'I wanted to be a solider. That was my dream. But a horse kicked me in the head. Didn't see that coming. Couldn't join up. Didn't want me. Other blokes were marching in the streets and protesting about Vietnam, and they were knocking me back.'

He shrugged his shoulders.

'So I found myself another dream. Galveston.'

He opened his eyes and smiled.

Again, Bob Hawke cackled his famous words.

'I loved listening to Glen Campbell sing that song about Galveston. 'Bout a soldier thinking of his home and his girlfriend and he's off fighting a war that they wouldn't let me fight in.'

He was talking about the Jimmy Webb song. And suddenly he started singing the title refrain over and over again.

Only a few lines and he was silent again.

He went to the esky and poured some more vile lime cordial. The Dog and I shook our heads when he offered us a swig from the bottle.

'I loved that song so much I went to the place. Saved up, went on a tour and made sure I went to visit Galveston. Just a dream I had.'

He took a pull from the bottle and briefly sounded like a dog with something caught in its throat. When he had regained composure, he continued. 'I went to Galveston…and there was nothing fucking there. Nothing. A shitload of nothing. Why the fella would sing about it, I don't know.'

The radio played the anthem of the America's Cup campaign, 'Down Under' by Men at Work.

'Yeah, we've all got dreams. But they can be funny things.'

Uncle Royce closed his eyes again and sat in silence. The wind picked up a bit and the flags flapped. I looked up at them and noticed that the boxing kangaroo Uncle Royce had threaded on the line to salute Australia's victory had been put on in celebratory haste. It fluttered happily enough, upside down.

It was a welcoming to a new era for Australia.

*5*

In 1986 Bob Hawke was still prime minister and still Tom Joading on the presentation stages of various sporting contests, still slapping backs and helping lift cups and trophies. Still revelling in his genuine love and appreciation of all things sport. Things were on the move, for not only had the America's Cup headed to its new home in Western Australia so, as it happened, had I.

The first person I saw and spoke to in the foyer of the Western Australian Academy of Performing Arts, an institution with the useful acronym WAAPA, was a soul who watched the foyer like a pleasant marsupial.

He was, in fact, a sad-eyed man from Adelaide with a mournful but polite and gracious manner, permed hair, an unfortunate nervous rash on his forehead and a unique opening line in conversation.

'I don't know about you but I can't wait to get into my leotard and sweat my tummy off.' He did something with his tongue and half smiled at me. This was Leotards' first encounter with a fellow acting student.

I can't remember what I said but I can remember what I was wearing. A pair of KingGee work shorts and an old Rugby jersey, so I can't imagine that much more was shared between us. He was, I could see, already in his leotard and wore a loose blue and white striped T-shirt like a French sailor in a bad Judy Garland movie.

The differences in our attire were stark. I thought that everyone would dress like Leotards and perhaps, in a fleeting moment of terror, he thought that everyone would dress like me.

The truth of course was somewhere between the two, falling more on the side of Leotards' electric blue leotard than my KingGees but roughly evening itself out over the three years of the course.

But we were yet to find that out. For the time being we had to wait.

Leotards waiting to start sweating and me waiting for god knows what.

How I had found myself in Western Australia was just one of those things.

Things were changing in the mid-eighties. The Hawke government, as well as celebrating all things sport, had enacted a raft of economic reforms and deregulation, opening up the Australian economy to the world.

More money flowed into and out of Australia. It was the beginning of easy international loans and the age of the entrepreneur was born.

People willing to make debt their friend and skim the margins were coming into their golden period.

Men like the folk hero Alan Bond and a host of other West Australians were doing well – Lang Hancock, Laurie Connell, Kerry Stokes and Robert Holmes à Court. All of them with varying degrees of skill and foresight were riding the wave of wealth. If a new merchant bank wasn't being announced it was a new media or resources company.

Perth's relationship with Australia in the eighties was a little like Australia's relationship with the world. It was affluent, isolated and increasingly cosmopolitan. It was a beautiful city with wide open, limitless horizons, yet it was also a place of great intolerance and suspicion of those who didn't belong.

That could range from anyone from the east – meaning the rest of Australia – to newly arrived immigrants from other areas of the globe.

Perth was of Western Australia, but also was not. It was a sprawling city hugging the coast in a vast state full of emptiness. It was a place that crossed many boundaries – the arsehole end of the earth but also a city where empires were being created, lost and born again.

Funnily enough as I looked at Leotards, and realised that even though he was wearing a loose sailor's shirt he would have to do an *immense* amount of sweating to make any dint in his 'tummy', I wasn't thinking about any of these things. The prospect of spending three years in Perth in close, and in some cases incredibly close, contact with a group of people who I had never met before and knew nothing about didn't make me feel overly enthusiastic about the life choice I had made.

I was supposed to be studying law. That seemed like a reasonable thing to do. Indeed my father had thought so.

'Jesus, there's hope for you yet!' he'd mumbled.

But it also seemed like a lot of hard work and when I was invited to make up the numbers in a drama course in Perth I decided to defer for a year and see what it was like to fart about in costumes.

My parents were incredibly supportive of my heartfelt desire.

'Bloody typical,' whispered my mother. 'For Christ's sake don't tell your father.'

When he did find out my father wished me all the best.

'No son of mine is going to be a pissed-upon actor,' he said, more in hurt than anything else.

I didn't tell him until the day I was about to leave and I think all he really wanted was to be told what was going on. The idea that anybody in Australia could make a living out of acting was also something he wasn't sure about.

'If you end up some raggedy-arsed bastard on a street corner shaking a tin, you pie-can, don't expect a blind bloody penny from me. Not even a bent one.'

Of course over the next three years there wasn't ever a time when my shaking tin wasn't filled by my parents, never a time when they would let me go without. But, true to form, my father never let it be thought that what I was doing was a good idea.

'He should have got a trade, for Christ's sake. One of them should have got a trade.'

'Well I suppose he's got to do something,' my mother said, staring hard.

My father shook his big head.

'Jeeeesuus wept. Well, stand tall, stand tall, for Christ's sake...
You might get parts as a butler.'

My mother brightened. 'Yes...yes...or maybe a mountie.'

So I left with my collection of Hawaiian shirts, Rugby jerseys
and work shorts and my parents' good wishes ringing in my
ears. I hopped on a bus without any air-conditioning that took
me across the Nullarbor and dropped me off in Perth, a lot
smellier and a lot less human than I was when I left.

For the first few weeks I was generously put up by a household
of lesbians who knew a friend of mine from Central Queensland.
They kindly fed me and wished me well as I embarked on my
theatrical training.

All this had taken me to the foyer with Leotards and I asked
myself whether a deferment for a year was too long. But, as it
is with those who simply float with life, if a strong current
catches you it's easier to drift and enjoy the journey.

I met my other classmates and was relieved to see that not
all dressed à la Leotards. But characters abounded. Pencils was
a thin, 120 percent committed enthusiast with an abundance
of courage and an intensity that could weld rivets in the Sydney
Harbour Bridge. He specialised in a staccato vocal delivery that
was full of energy and enunciated every syllable, and then some
he seemed to invent on his own.

Fascinatin' was charming and instantly likeable, a ladies' man
who would utter the word fascinatin' over and over again in
response to all manner of subjects.

A woman's eyes were, 'Fascinatin', truly fascinatin'.'

And at the same time the texture and smell of a devon
sandwich was equally, 'Fascinatin', truly fascinatin'.'

Sahara was one of my good friends and a fellow KingGee wearer, although he went for trousers instead of shorts. He had gained a certain immortality in my eyes as he'd been part of the Eastern Suburbs A-grade Rugby team that went through a season without a win. He was called Sahara because of his tendency to occasionally 'dry' – a term used to describe an actor forgetting lines.

His dries were so epic they were deemed to be desert-like and so the legend of Sahara was born.

There were others: Lardy MacBeth, Piggy Scum, the Mauler, Spiderwoman, Birdman, The Berserk Warrior and my good friends, Nile and Leon.

We were all thrust into the world of culture. A week-long workshop to produce a disastrous *Richard the Third* was designed to show us just how much we had to learn, which was plenty. I sounded like some old actor from *The Dam Busters* for that is how I thought Shakespeare was to be 'acted'. I was only outdone by Pencils who kept on getting the people he had killed and those he was yet to kill, and a couple of people from other plays of Shakespeare who were killed, all mixed up; and dear old Sahara who, when it was his turn to pretend to be Richard sitting alone with his demons before his last battle at Bosworth Field, started off comfortably and then rolled his eyes and half smiled like a dog getting the part of its tummy it can't reach scratched.

'Oh, sorry mate…gone, completely gone,' muttered Sahara with a shrug as if yet another Easts Rugby match had gone down the gurgler.

The battle scene at the end was a collection of people who had raided the workshop of prop swords and the ensuing melee was more like a Depression strike-breaking riot with bits and pieces of treated pine flying around the room as timber was swung and hurled with gusto.

As luck would have it the Perth Festival was on at the same time, and indicating the particular global characteristic of the new Australia, a Georgian theatre company, The Rustavelis, were touring a production of *Richard the Third*.

The production was freed from the self-conscious importance and reverie that we had so eccentrically exhibited as, if truth be told, had so many more pompous and grand theatrical productions. It was free from the tradition of the English text. The Rustavelis, we were told by the press and our teachers, were from behind the Iron Curtain. Part of the Soviet Union and, therefore, we all thought, Russian.

So we all gloried in the performance, in the depth of their talent, the richness of their voices and went home thinking that of course all they do is act, just like all those Russian gymnasts and athletes – they don't have proper jobs, don't have to worry about making a crust, they just have to worry about making art.

Someone at the academy had the bright idea of inviting some of the Rustavelis back after a performance. Nearly all of them came and, for an evening, we stood and watched Russian communists up close.

They all wore very odd clothes, not great Cossack hats or military braid, or any other cliché that could be readily grabbed, but cardigans and sandals and even some Wham! 'Think Big' T-shirts.

They drank a fair bit and didn't speak much English, but sang and put on a concert for us that was so immense in its talent, content and warmth that even today I don't think the vast depth of their performance could be appreciated by any who saw it.

They weren't, as it turned out, Russian at all, but Georgian, with a separate history and culture that was only hinted at. At one point a Rustaveli started singing a song. From around the room all the others joined in – voices soaring across the tonal scale, and the warmth and layered texture was immensely moving.

I didn't understand what was being sung, but the emotion created was so powerful that after the song was finished a silence, a true silence, hung around the room.

A Rustaveli with a Wham T-shirt held a bottle of vodka out for me to drink. I accepted and he bellowed in broken English, 'Tonight…you…me…only you me… No countries… Sing.'

They were inviting us to sing, to give them a piece of our culture. Inside the concert hall of the academy, an institution that was the centre for all disciplines of the arts, an institution that would resound to students playing the music of the world's great composers, of dance students performing great ballets of the world and drama students bastardising the great plays, I waited to see what would be offered.

Senior students gathered in a circle and began to sing our offering.

'Kookaburra sits in the old gum tree…'

Nobody save for the seven or so singers made any noise.

We all sat in our seats. In a place of learning, a place of the arts, we had nothing save a kindy song to offer.

A voice from a nearby seat said, without a trace of irony, 'Makes you feel proud, doesn't it?'

The Wham-wearing Rustaveli looked at me, smiled, shrugged his shoulders and offered me another slug of vodka.

'You are young...lots of time to find your music.'

Perhaps we could have taken that as a challenge. We were, after all, embarking on our education in the arts. A few months later the most successful Australian film ever made was released. *Crocodile Dundee.* Complete with laughing kookaburras.

While the students were all a little larger than life, we had nothing on the staff. Most of our teachers were wonderful, professional practitioners of theatre. Geoff Gibbs was the dean and his never-ending good humour and modesty gave an indication of just what was needed to survive the roller-coaster of a life in the creative arts. 'Whatever else happens, William,' he said as we sat eating Pollywaffle chocolate bars one lunch break, 'never take yourself too seriously. Take the work seriously but not yourself. Life is too much fun to disappear up your own arse.'

Aarne Neeme was the head of drama and was the hardest working and most honourable man I think I have ever met in theatre.

There were others too, Robyn Payne and Annie Steiner and the rest of the set teachers were patient and, just like us, wanting to make a go of it. They were a little more jaundiced perhaps by the years they had spent in the profession but they cared enough to let us believe there was a future and that what we were doing was worthwhile. We'd all been plucked from the suburbs of our great nation and were given the benefit of a unique collection of expert tutelage.

Our time at the academy coincided with the beginning of New-Age ideas of health, movement and life. This was basically a boon for old hippies and odd bods who suddenly found some use for their dabbling in massage, yoga and any variants of said 'disciplines'.

Where else but a drama school in Perth would you find them?

The movement teachers were the most entertaining and we had Tai Chi, contact, massage, Feldenkrais and meditation.

Tai Chi Dave was a beauty. A master in fact. A master of Tai Chi. These days you get Masters in Business and Commerce, back then we had a Master in Tai Chi.

Dave was a tall man who dressed in baggy black, was bald but with a GI Joe beard, smelt suitably of incense and spat when he spoke in his outrageous Cockney accent.

He made Michael Caine sound like Prince Charles as he would try to tell us the basics of Tai Chi.

'It's a martial yart, a martial yart, dat's what tis. A marshal yart, a mystic martial yart. Fancy dat.'

He may have been a Tai Chi master but he had a name that was about as mystic as a Morris Minor. Dave Lane, Tai Chi master with the manner of a market seller from *Mary Poppins*.

He would hold up faded yellow photos of other, older Tai Chi masters.

'Him 'ere, he's a marster, famous Tai Chi marster. 'Ere, 'ow old you fink 'e is den? Hmm?'

Nobody said anything.

'Remember, 'e's a marster! Keeps fit, like a worrier. 'Ow old?'

Nobody said anything because we all wanted so very much to be right, even in Tai Chi Dave's lesson. Finally Pencils voiced a syllable-rattling guess.

'He...issssssss seeev-vennnnn-teeeeee-fiiiive!'

'Wrong, 'e is one hundred and firteen.' He picked up another photo of another 'marster'.

''Ow old's he? C'mon, c'mon 'ow old you fink 'e is?'

Pencils went again.

'Niiiiiii-nnnnn-teee-two?'

'Wrong 'e's hundred and twenty-five. And 'e's a worrier.'

We were, it seemed, not in touch with the earth.

'You're not 'n touch wiv de earf. Dat's wot your problem is. Git 'n touch wiv de earf.'

We were guided across the road to the municipal park where we removed our shoes and engaged the earth.

Dave scratched his arse, peered around and mumbled, 'Got to git 'n touch wiv de earf.'

He proceeded to strike a pose and we craned our way in formation across the grass.

''Member, it's important to keep hold of the worrier wifin,' said Dave.

Unfortunately we were Tai Chi-ing across a piece of grass that hadn't been mown by the council and was riddled with a collection of bindies, little prickles with nasty teeth, and Dave's floating crane pose turned into a rather painful and desperate spurt of manic Irish Dancing.

'Ooooo, fuck! Worrier spirit, keep hold the worrier spirit – ooo bugger.'

The people in front thought that Dave's exertions were part of the lesson and followed him.

Dave's other great claim to fame was his skill as an iridologist.

He put on his best spruiker's manner and addressed us one class.

'Now as it 'appens, I yam a marster of de eyes. I can tell you 'bout yourself fro' lookin' at your eyes.'

'Tell me about myself,' said Fascinatin' in the manner of someone out of a bad movie about knights and witches. Fascinatin' liked to describe himself as Irish and was very much in touch with the mythology of the Celts, which meant he walked about wearing Manchester United gear on most occasions. It was impossible not to like him, and if there was ever a man who should have worn a sword it was he, for he always walked like he had one.

But Tai Chi Dave had already decided that Nile, who was sitting happily enough in the sun, would be his target.

'You...' stared Dave

'Yes, Dave,' said Nile in a polite deadpan.

'Hmm, you've got...you've got summit wrong wiv your penis...'

'Well thank you, Dave, for the time you've taken in sharing that with me...and the rest of the class,' deadpanned Nile.

Fascinatin' stared at Dave. He didn't seem too keen on Tai Chi Dave's ten-second consultations anymore. Especially where Fascinatin's recreation was concerned.

'You should go see a VD clinic,' Dave laughed.

Nile's eyebrows twitched a little.

'Dave, I hear you...as do the rest of the class.'

I had no idea if it was a joke of Dave's.

'Fascinatin', Dave,' said Facsinatin' and I think if he had had a sword he would have used it. Instead he half bowed. 'But now I no longer wish to know about myself.' And under his breath, he added, 'This guy's a fucking pillock.'

But Dave wasn't alone. There was Gavin the meditation teacher. He was, as it turned out, a Buddhist monk who spoke with a lisp and sounded like Dave's cousin. Gavin added his own particular touch – a shortened hum at the end of most sentences. Whether this was supposed to indicate his wisdom or constant questioning of our consciousness, I don't know. All I know is that he did it so often that after a while he sounded like a large, bearded guinea pig. I have no idea where these folk came from but there were a lot of ex-pat English making up the population of Perth so maybe the Pommy mystics came at a good price.

Gavin would talk about the Him-marrr-liath. Hummmmmm. Meaning the Himalayas. And we underwent a series of classes where we would hold hands and hum and stand in a circle and chant to a candle.

'I give you my love and give you my heart. You are the god of heavenly light.' And we would walk and bow towards the candle. When it was my turn I noticed that the candle had an inscription around the bottom.

I took it to be the chant we were calling out and the next time I got closer to have a look. 'Made in Taiwan' was the message.

Well, it was the burgeoning age of globalisation.

The massage teacher was a gentle man with an enormous beard and a gentle voice to match his nature. In fact it was so gentle we had trouble hearing. He taught the unique concept of self-massage and warned us that massage could release great and unseen parts of our body and mind.

I didn't know what parts of the body would release what as I only heard every third word.

'Elbow…hmmmmmmph…deep…mmmmmmmmmm…toes…idea…mother…spirit.' And he would smile his lovely sweet smile.

The idea of massaging someone you hardly knew was a little much to take and, on some days, it was like dancing classes in little school. You stuck immediately with what you thought was a safe bet.

The problem, of course, was that this didn't always work out and I had to endure an hour and a half of rubbing some almost-stranger's bits and bobs.

I had no idea where to put what and on one truly sad occasion my kneading of someone's back was eliciting the strangest sounds from their stomach and I knew the whole process wasn't going to end happily.

Our teacher, the Sweet Mumbler, indicated some movement was required with one of the legs of my unfortunate massagee. I attempted to follow the instructions, and as I looked around to see if I was doing something vaguely in the right area, I saw a room full of people looking as if they were all at wells and pumping for water. Or it was as if the back pages of my Dux exercise books had come to life and a room full of people were contorting prone victims in a homage to resuscitation diagrams.

The primordial rumblings coming from the massagee's stomach built into a cacophony of farts, moans and groans which truly seemed to render any relaxation and subconscious benefits completely moot.

The Sweet Mumbler smiled and nodded.

'Mmmmmphmmmmmm deep…mummmbblemmmmmumble…subconscious…hooofffffff…need.'

The idiot I was manipulating got up after the session and, grabbing a bottle of oil, said that my touch was very different from the touch of a lover.

I stared at Leotards and tried to think what to say.

'Well, mate, I suppose that's only right. I mean I'm not your lover and I don't really think this is supposed to be about getting a root.'

He stared at me mournfully and his rash seemed to be crimson.

'Just an observation, William.'

Fascinatin' and Sahara giggled and I nodded.

Two rows down an Irish girl, who was completely repelled by any thought of human contact, lay there looking for all the world like a corpse. A great awkward, red-headed man loomed over her like a stick insect.

'Come on, come on, for Christ's sake, just rub wherever... Ahh Christ,' she growled. 'Keep yourself nice or I'll bite yerr fuckin' hand right off.'

For all I knew these classes might be the only physical contact some of these people would ever have. I didn't actually know who was who and who liked what. We could have been oiling and rubbing passengers on a peak-hour train for as much good it did.

The Alexander Technique and the Feldenkrais movement method were also disciplines we were introduced to.

They were both designed to rediscover ways of moving. The former originating from a Tasmanian who was a 'raging root rat' according to Tai Chi Dave and the latter from an Israeli soccer player.

There was another movement teacher who was half woman, half vinyl couch.

She dressed in PVC and cheap leather, and when she walked around your prone body it sounded like wet wallpaper sheets peeling off the wall in the middle of the night.

Her jewellery banged and clanked as she manipulated limbs and arms.

She spoke about consciousness, letting go and imagining, but she made it sound like Madge the old Palmolive dishwashing-liquid saleswoman. 'You know you're soaking in it!'

The Feldenkrais teachers sounded vaguely transpacific and were always very neat and well-dressed. 'We're going to teach you how to rediscover your body and how it moves.'

We did a lot of standing up and sitting down and, as I remember it, sleeping. In fact we slept so much we called it Feldensnooze. The teachers just seemed to give up and not come anymore.

I suppose movement was a little airy fairy and that is certainly what we got from Annie Steiner who was the head of movement.

After the *Richard the Third* effrontery we had a movement project in which we were encouraged to pick a fairytale character and dress and behave like that character when we met in a pre-determined destination, in this case the sunken gardens at the beautiful University of Western Australia campus.

Fair enough, but I had chosen Paul Bunyan and, complete with an axe and Canadian lumberjack apparel, was yelling out like a loon with a bad Canadian accent about 'Cuttin' doon trees' and calling for my moose.

Paul Bunyan had, I remembered from some story, a moose, a pet moose. Anyway that would have been okay, except that I had to catch a bus and train to get to the sunken gardens.

Perth was a clean and pleasant city with lots of well-dressed, pleasant people. Nobody really said anything when I sang my lumberjack songs and called for my moose; save one old lady who I helped onto a bus to Nedlands.

'Your axe needs a good drop of linseed oil if you want to do any good against a tree, dear.'

In the middle of the city, as I walked to the railway station, I could see the building that was to be the headquarters of Bond Corporation. It was a massive towering declaration of Alan Bond's and Western Australia's success.

Perth was home to a gang of millionaires and a successful and popular premier – Brian Burke – who was one of the new can-do Labor politicians.

Perth even had a connection to Bob Hawke. Although not born there he grew up in Perth and graduated from the University of Western Australia, and his uncle had been premier of the state in the 1950s.

It seemed if you walked the streets in the eighties dressed as a lumberjack with a bad accent searching for your moose, Perth was the place to be.

Even though the drama school seemed to be all encompassing, the outside world wasn't that far away. I moved from the household of Lesbos to take up residence in a house just down the way from the academy. Two seemingly peaceful, long-haired Alternative Lifestyles lived there.

The house had a nice big garden, some of which was turned over for the cultivation of various bits of vegetation. Some, like the zucchinis, were generously doled out to me but other produce was more secretly guarded and used to supplement the income of the Alternatives.

They were a nice couple, Andrew and his Portuguese wife Jane, and it was none of my business if they made a bit of pocket money from some recreational growth in the garden.

These suburban transactions meant that there was a steady stream of people coming and going, and it was quite hard to keep track of who was who. Andrew was at first a bit circumspect about his dealings in front of me, but when he worked out that I didn't really care he would chat about how many drop-ins he'd had that day as we ate some roasted zucchini.

'Good thing about you, Willy, is that you look like a cop. Which is sort of nice. Calms people down.'

I couldn't quite work out why this would, but I nodded and ate more zucchini.

Most of the Alternatives' customers didn't really hang around too long, they would knock on the door, fidget in the kitchen, hand over the money and nick off.

There were all sorts – people in pastel suits, tradies, students and people who looked like they had just walked in from the Cuban revolution.

Sometimes it was a tall man who would stay for a cup of tea and play with the couple's big moggie, who was called Bishe, after a Hindi god. The tall man would talk about one subject.

Conversations, which were all one-way, would be about him. Or, to be more precise, his body. He couldn't figure out why he had freckles on his shoulders and nowhere else.

At first I didn't even know he was talking to me. He'd just sit there stroking the cat, sipping his tea and listing parts of his body that were freckle-free.

'None on my arms. None on my stomach. None on my legs. None on my feet. None anywhere, not even a mole. Nothing. But why are they on my shoulders?' Then he'd get up and go.

There was another customer who was always talking about how things were booming. How Australia was changing. He had a name tag on his shirt: Warrick.

I was making a cup of tea and I thought I would make some sort of conversation.

'What part of the bank do you work in, Warrick?'

He looked like he'd been stung by a hornet.

'How do you know my name? Did Andrew tell you? What do you do?'

'I'm a student up at the academy and you've got a name tag with a bank logo on it.'

Warrick stared at me, nodded and took off his name tag. He never wore it again.

It turned out he worked in finance and planning, and he could see a whole new world opening up.

'Sometime people will be able to move money wherever they want. Between cash, funds and shares. It'll be a liquid economy; it'll be wonderful.'

He was like a flipside of Andrew and Jane and the teachers at the academy.

'This government we've got here is sensational, simply sensational. They're great because they're Labor – but they are so far in the money that it means the whole shape of politics is changing. Men like Keating and Burke – they're engineering a new Australia.'

The big boon was that the 'lefties had to prove they were careful with the pennies' and so socialism was dead.

I told him I didn't think it had ever even existed in Australia.

'Well, either way, we don't want it anyway. Because these guys, you know, these guys like Bond and Skase they're the new pioneers. They're leading the way.'

Andrew didn't say much during Warrick's visits, just nodded a bit and drank his green tea.

The only time he would spark up was when the conversation ran to football. Australian Rules football. Jane didn't like Andrew listening to it because it was too much about aggression. 'It's either that or she just doesn't get the game.'

So he would go and hide behind his mull plants and quietly listen to the games on a transistor radio. His team was the Subiaco Lions and he would gasp in whispers and moan quietly depending on their fortunes.

'Too aggressive, too aggressive,' shouted Jane.

Andrew would look sheepish, brush the hair from his eyes and pretend to tend the garden.

The next day he made some tea for one of his drop-ins and talked a bit of sport.

'But I see it as just chasing. A big game of chasey. I loved playing chasey. Something elemental about it all – even the kicking. It's great to be able to release your spirit through games.'

Warrick also loved football but supporting a suburban team was too passé for him. He was planning on becoming a member of Western Australia's newly formed national footy team who would later be known as the West Coast Eagles.

'Old style footy is going. Waste of time. Markets too small, there is no scope for growth. The club is already so cashed up it'll win a flag in a few seasons. It's groundbreaking.'

'What do you mean?' said Andrew.

'It's more of a business than a club, you'll be able to own a part of a business. Fantastic.'

Warrick opened a *Daily News* he had carried in. 'How's the form of these fucking idiots?'

He held up the front page. 'Barlow and Chambers Hanged' was emblazoned across the tabloid.

Kevin Barlow and Brian Chambers were hanged that day in Malaysia for drug trafficking, after a long and protracted series of appeals and pleas for clemency from Bob Hawke. I looked at a photo of Kevin Barlow. He didn't look that much older than we three sitting there sipping tea.

'What do you mean?' said Andrew after a while.

Warrick took a great intake of breath and jiggled his hands together. His tone was the same as when he spoke about the football.

'Well they both knew, both, what the penalties were. Nobody asked them to trade drugs, they were stupid enough and got caught. End of story. Don't feel sorry for them at all. Do the crime do the time. It's just business, don't have to make it into a cause.'

There was a pause as Andrew sipped his tea. He put his cup on the table.

'Warrick...man, I think you should buy your drugs somewhere else,' he said gently.

Warrick smiled and his mouth twitched as he half laughed. 'What you mean?'

'I mean I don't mind you coming here in your bank uniform and talking about the world that's coming, but, man, have some humility. Don't talk about it being business when these guys are dead and you sit there with a bag of dope you are gonna smoke. It's just...not what I want in my world.'

Warrick flushed a little, smiled and stood up. 'Plenty of other places to buy, Andrew.'

He bent back down to pick up the bag of grass that had just fallen out of his pocket along with his bank name tag and a silver pen. Then he nodded and walked down the hall out to the front door. Andrew called after him, 'Your football team of the future sucks.'

We sat for a while looking down at the front page of the paper Warrick had left behind.

'If that's the future that just walked out of the house then, man, we are racing towards a precipice. Hope I don't meet the future again, no, not in a hurry for the future.'

As it turned out I did happen to cross paths with the future. The America's Cup defence had been taking place since late in my first year at the academy and the whole world, or what people in Perth like to think of as the world, seemed to have descended upon the city.

Namely lots of Americans and Europeans who dressed like the ads in *Harper's Bazaar* and *Vanity Fair*. Lots of brand names, sunglasses and teeth.

Perth was used to having lots of visitors from overseas – usually members of the American navy who would rumble ashore for some rest and recreation. They all seemed to be incredibly immense people, different from the magazine ads of the American Cup aficionados. They were black and white and as they rolled through the streets with their short hair, glasses and jeans pulled high with the cuffs tucked into their sneakers, they appeared to be from another planet.

Once in a nightclub a man with a head like a torpedo loomed up to me and a few friends and asked if he could drink with us. He was from some big ship parked down at Fremantle and he was just out on the town with a few buddies.

He thought we looked like guys he could have a drink with and learn a little about Australia.

Americans always seemed like they were playing some game but they never were, never once in any of the dealings I have had with them then and since have they ever had any trace of irony.

They were 'straight and down people, just doing a job for their country'.

The Torpedo, who was about seven and a half feet high and ten feet wide, was called Tommy and that such a little boy's name could be given to a human being so big was slightly unsettling.

So was his polite and courteous manner.

I asked him what the job was that he was doing for his country.

'Why we're protecting America.' He smiled and added as an afterthought, 'And our allies...you guys.'

Protecting us from what?

'From the bad guys. Yes, sir, they are out there.' He pointed to the dance floor, 'Somewhere,' and laughed.

'You know we have so much weaponry on board our old boat that we could blow you guys right from the bottom of the world to the top. Sort of humbling to have that power. Got to know how to use it.'

The fact we were studying drama was of minor interest.

'Why?'

None of us could really answer.

For myself I felt embarrassed to admit that I thought becoming an actor was something worthwhile. Especially to this American. Even though he may have appeared to me as a cliché, he and his country had demonstrated it was their world we were visiting, even here in a bad nightclub in Perth. He came from a utensil of military destruction that could destroy the city we were living in tenfold. It was all right to think of him as a joke, but he and his kind had their fingers on the button.

'Do you people make movies down here? They should teach you to talk like us. Then you could get jobs in America. You know we make the best movies, got the best actors. We invented movies. Guess that's why it's so.'

'You got the best,' I said.

Torpedo Tommy nodded. He looked at us and had a drink. 'You know the problem is everybody wants to be American. Even people who don't like us want to be us. That is what we are stopping. Hard to know how to do it, but I guess a boatload of weaponry is as best a way as any.'

I asked Torpedo Tommy what he actually did on his boat.

'Sir, I am a plumber,' he said. He stood up, for it was obvious that he had learnt enough about Australia, but he turned to us before he rejoined his buddies and their high-hitched jeans and their whiter than white shoes.

'You guys should play more sports. That's what my dad said you were good at when I told him I was coming here. He said you were great at tennis. Don't know myself. And you got our Cup!' he laughed. 'And we're coming back for it!'

And indeed they were. High atop Perth in Kings Park an American breakfast television show called *The Today Show* had set up a studio broadcasting news and events and meaningless chitchat back to America. People would gather in the night to watch them talk about American events, American weather, and interviewing people about what was happening that day just down the corner. Meaning somewhere in America. And here the pancaked, made-up pair sat on the highest part of the most isolated city in the world as far away as possible from America you could geographically get.

'The world is coming to Perth but it still wants to be where it is from.' That is what Tai Chi Dave said. 'You fink dat's mad? Well that's imperialism is all 'bout. Madness. Makes no sense.'

It would have been nice if Dave could have been asked to give a bit of an eye-reading on the midnight *Today* show but sadly he never got the chance.

It didn't seem to matter whether Dave was right, there were times when all the images combined to mark a surreal moment.

On a beach in Fremantle a crowd had gathered to watch a sort of cultural smorgasbord of a festival for the America's Cup. Horsemen from Italy dressed in dream-like renaissance robes and porcelain face masks galloped at full speed along the sand and then thrust a sword through a small card. The clouds were rolling in slightly, and although there was light along the bottom of the wide horizon, it had a slightly trippy quality according to my companion, a ballet dancer who had an interesting habit of stretching her long legs.

The horizon seemed filled with the great dark bulk of the USS *Missouri*, the American battleship that squatted in the water like a great angry toad. Its huge guns pointing toward the festival.

I wondered if Torpedo Tommy was down in its bowels making sure its plumbing was humming along.

One of the horsemen speared the card and his horse reared as a helicopter landed nosily on the pad set up at one end of the beach. Somebody behind me said, 'It's like something out of a James Bond movie.'

On the street above came the amplified sound of buskers and somebody playing panpipes in some sort of South American tune.

We walked up to where the music blared and were confronted by a pair of people in medieval dress. A big knight and a little skinny knight. The big knight had a long staff and was hitting the bejesus out of the little knight, who had a sad little bent sword. In fact he hit him so hard that the little knight's helmet, complete with a pair of antlers, was twirling around on his head. There was a muffled cry of 'Shit go easy, Reg' from underneath the revolving antlers.

The buskers stopped with the pipe music and started singing 'Quando Quando Quando'.

'Oh I love Inca music!' sang my ballet dancer and she did a graceful little dance that drew some admiring glances from a clutch of *Harper's Bazaar* and *Vanity Fair* people.

'Oh well,' drawled one older American woman who had a face that looked like it was in a permanent wind tunnel, 'at least they speak English and you can drink the water.'

It should have been a humbling experience to hear your nation being conveniently patronised by a visitor, but what was the point? They would all be gone soon.

The ballet dancer received a little round of applause, laughed and took my hand. A large white car rolled past and someone yelled to a man in the back.

'Good on you, Burkey!'

Brian Burke, the West Australian premier, waved as the window was slowly rolled up. 'God bless you,' he said as the window covered up his face. His voice sounded not unlike Bob Santamaria. Bob was a bald-headed man from the National Civic Council. A disaffected leftover from the ALP split of the fifties, he would come on the telly for five minutes before the Sunday midday movie and politely rant against Gough Whitlam and the Labor Party.

Overhead a plane with a message in lights flew low: 'Enjoy alfresco at Mexico City.'

I was looking up at it laughing when a hand that wasn't the ballet dancer's took mine.

I looked down to see an Indigenous Australian. He had an epically black eye and smelled of urine and beer.

He wanted some money to get a train to Midland.

I gave him some change from my pocket and watched him sway and saunter off down the street. The band still played, the plane above flashed its message and I held the hand of the ballet dancer.

'Pretty trippy,' she said. The world had certainly come to Perth.

But it was all over in a week. The Americans came and took back their Cup.

Alan Bond didn't get a chance to be the rich tubby man to defend the Cup. Another even tubbier rich man called Kevin Parry had a boat called *Kookaburra* that was chosen to race for the prize.

Two fat skippers with zinc cream wrapped around their mouths and wearing bad sunglasses steered the big yachts around the coast in the blue waters of the Indian Ocean.

We'd gone to the beach down at Cottesloe and swam out to the old pylon after the deciding race and stayed for a drink at the pub.

Nobody seemed very happy, as if a party had finished too early. As the ballet dancer and I squeezed into a small car I saw the future. There sitting on the kerb was Warrick. He was plastered. He sat with his head in his jiggling hands. I was going to call out his name but I thought better of it.

He raised his head, looked straight at us but didn't recognise me and yelled out, 'Outstanding... Outstanding' and then he vomited like a broken fire hydrant.

'Oh pretty trippy,' said my companion.

The end of the party didn't take that long to spread. In mid 1987 'pretty trippy' could have been aptly used to describe the federal election. If eccentric characters abounded around the halls of the academy then they were matched by the halls of power. Johannes Bjelke-Petersen, the premier of Queensland, actively launched a campaign to become prime minister. Effectively he split the coalition in two, promising to start a bushfire that would sweep the nation and end up with a new conservative party which he would generously lead.

Although Joh himself opted out of the whole contest when he smelt the decay of his ambition, the idea that he could achieve this and that people like a collection of white-shoed entrepreneurs should follow him was unnerving evidence of how political leaders can misread the public mood and their own long-term value.

Undoubtedly a success in Queensland politics, there were too many checks and balances that ranged across the nation, like a questioning press and the sceptics who laughed at the idea of a Queenslander becoming prime minister.

'It's not him being a Queenslander that's a problem,' said my father down the phone line, 'it's the fact that he comes from bloody outer space these days. Believes his own farts. It'll end in tears.'

The federal Liberal Party was led by John Howard who looked in this mid-political life incarnation not so much like a Thunderbird but more like one of the puppets that the Tracy boys saved.

He wore a comb-over that Doug Anthony would be proud of and glasses the size of Greek dinner plates. On the face of it, he seemed as far away as possible from the wavy haired lairism of Bob Hawke. But they were oddly similar in a suburban sense. While Hawke was the suburban jock par excellence, Howard was just as recognisable a suburban icon, the consistent trier. The stayer. The fellow who worked tirelessly on the sausage sizzle of life. He'd sit on any committee, be a part of any working bee and litter army.

He was a man who was living in the hedonistic high-flying 1980s and doing an impersonation of enjoying it. The fact that he prospered enough to be leader of the opposition for four years was a remarkable testament to his capacity to work and survive. That and the fact that he was a lot tougher and cunning than he looked.

He was lumbered with a polite but listless Treasury spokesman – Jim Carlton – who looked like Godfrey from *Dad's Army*.

The tax policy imploded a day after it was launched and, added to the demented 'Joh for PM' campaign, Howard never really had a chance. So like some poor sad pantomime the election was played out. Bob Hawke crossing the country delivering speeches to his friends and fellow Australians. Paul Keating, a well-dressed knife, muttering about fiscal illiterates in the Liberals, and Howard bravely waffling on against the tide.

We were told by both parties that it was an historic election, as we were always told, but it differed in a way from its predecessors. Hawke's Tom Joading around the presentation stages of the nation gave him a huge back-catalogue of great achievements to slice into the flag-waving advertisements.

'We' even had a Wimbledon tennis champion courtesy of Pat Cash beating Ivan Lendl, a sure sign that we were mixing a little bit of mid-sixties sporty success with our new entrepreneurial get-up-and-go.

Hawke was identified with such victories, even though Cash did a showy strip and flung his shirt to the crowd and then proceeded to climb through the crowd to the player's box. It was just a young Australian champion celebrating in true-blue style.

All John Howard had was his eyebrows and teeth. People actually felt sorry for him, but there was no point in changing horses in midstream, as the Labor Party's peculiar jingle reminded us, and so we didn't.

My father asked the by-now-familiar question. 'Getting involved, son?' he said wistfully. 'Handing out any cards?'

I admitted that no, I was not getting involved but I was going to have an election do. I had no intention of doing so up until that phone call with him but I thought it might make him a bit happier.

There was a pause down the phone. 'Righto then...here's your mum again.'

As the phone was changed over I heard my father say, 'Not bloody interested in the slightest.'

'Well,' said my mother, 'you've made his day.'

'Well I am a bit busy, Mum.'

'Oh that'd be right. Did you see the crush in the shopping centre?'

I said I hadn't.

My mother told me that at a shopping centre appearance in Parramatta a riot had ensued when the Johnny Young *Young Talent Time* team had appeared.

'The people went barking. Pushing and shoving and then the silly bloody man who runs the shops said he hadn't seen anything like that, not even the Beatles.'

'What does that say about the Beatles then?' I said.

'What does it say about Parramatta is more the question. Imagine carrying on like headless chooks about Johnny Bloody Young. Really.'

Well it was the 1980s and so much for the global stage we strutted on. I wonder if Tommy Torpedo and the wind-tunnel American woman had watched *Young Talent Time*.

'Now make sure you do something for the campaign, won't you?' my mum asked.

I was as good as my word. The hairy Alternatives, Andrew and Jane, had packed and moved to Portugal so I was, for the moment, the only tenant of the house.

The vast backyard was mine and so I planned an epic event – a bonfire.

I even designed a Guy Fawkes type creature that I christened Bob, as in Bob Menzies. It seemed a bit low back then to burn poor old Howard and a waste of time to make a Joh for the flames.

No, it needed something nice. I thought about the founder of the Liberal Party being flung on the flames.

I also borrowed a television from my mate Leon. It was an epic old Chrysler with a chorded remote control. It weighed a ton and when you switched the channel it sounded like a bowling alley.

I pinched a few of the election signs and stuck them around the yard. Then I went to the State Library to photocopy old images from previous elections. I was collecting past trophies of the Liberal Party to burn in celebration. Well, that was the idea. I got bored after a while and, even though a fair few Harold Holt ads and even dear old Billy Snedden and his youthful crew got a roll out, I settled instead on a collection of underwear advertisements from a tabloid newspaper that I found amusing. The ads were a serious attempt to sell men meshed cotton action underwear. 007 underpants and singlets.

So with the backyard set up I waited for the action to take place.

Unfortunately it was July and the academy was on mid year holidays and almost everybody had left town. Most of my mates had flown back to eastern states, so there was nobody to invite.

I put a notice on a student board to see what that might bring and decided to cater for a few.

Spurred on by my father I intended to celebrate in style, so I bought as many prawns as I could and a couple of cartons of beer.

On the way back from the fish markets at Fremantle I remember stopping off to fill up the car I had borrowed from Leon.

A Fiat Bambino. The station I pulled into was a Povey petroleum company, yet another example of a zealous piece of entrepreneurialism. Mark Povey had a series of independent servos that were sprouting cheap petrol everywhere and this particular one on the Stirling Highway was being attended by the Povettes, a group of young women in white T-shirts and high-cut shorts.

It was cheap in more than one sense. A young woman whom I took to be one of the Povettes said my car was cute.

It wasn't my car but I wasn't going to tell her that.

I paid for my petrol in student change and said I was having a party tonight and she was more than welcome.

So I sat amidst my 007 underpants advertisements with a stockinged figure chock-full of old rags sitting next to me and I lit the fire, and waited for the crowds to come.

I was at about the bottom of my first bucket of prawns and making steady headway though the beer when I had my first inkling of the night's lack of success. I knew that not too many people were going to be coming so I started talking to Bob Menzies.

I asked his opinion about the fire.

'Need some more fuel if you're going to burn tonight, Bob.' I looked around and threw on a couple of the election signs but they burnt too quickly to be of any real good.

The yard was big so I decided that the neighbouring fence could do without a few pickets.

'That'll be the ticket, Bob.' And I staggered off into the dark to gather some pickets.

I began to quite like Bob and mentioned to him that it was nothing personal about me wanting to burn him.

It was cold. So I sat in front of the fire with an old black-and-white television cuddling Bob Menzies.

That's when I had my first visitor.

Murray, a baritone from the academy, had seen the message on the noticeboard. He'd bought a bottle of green ginger wine. He at least had been handing out how-to-vote cards for the Labor Party.

I didn't know Murray that well but he was more than welcome. The election was playing out to a victory to Labor with an increased majority and I admitted to Murray that I didn't want to burn Bob.

'I think he'd like to dance. Bit of music, Murray.'

Murray the baritone stood and drank his green ginger wine and sang a song full of 'hey nonny nonnies' and woods and merrily doing something or other, and I, for whatever reason known to myself, danced with Bob Menzies.

It was mid-dance when I had my second visitor.

'Hello?' came an uncertain voice from around the side of the house as I tried to jitterbug with Bob to Murray's vibrato-filled 'hey nonny nonnies'.

I held Bob and turned to see the Povette and a few friends. She stared at me and Murray. And Bob.

'We're going well,' I said. 'And I don't want to burn Bob.' Then I added, remembering my duties as host, 'Would you like some prawns?'

I introduced the group to Murray.

'She's a Povette,' I said pointing to my new friend.

'What do you mean?' she said.

Her tone meant that perhaps I had been jumping to conclusions.

'I'm not a Povette.'

There were things I could have said. Like, 'Oh, I'm sorry.' Instead I summoned all of my charm.

'Then why would you dress yourself like that if you weren't going to get paid?'

She looked at me and her rather large male friend took a step towards me.

I tried to recover. 'Now would you like some prawns?' I repeated with my voice rising slightly.

It turned out she didn't but one of her burly friends took a handful and they left soon, muttering 'fucking weirdo perverts' as they retreated down the side of the house.

Murray thanked me and decided it was time for him to go when Richard Carleton said that they were crossing to Paul Keating's backyard. It didn't look very much like mine and I watched Keating mumble in an unusually modest way about feeling humbled by the trust that had been given to the Labor Party.

'Think I'll watch Hawkie make his speech at home,' Murray said.

Me and Bob waved goodbye.

My last visitors of the night were the most entertaining. The neighbour had quite rightly taken exception to my election night do. It wasn't the burning of his fence, or the noise of the television and Murray's singing, it was what I was up to with my sex doll.

Now Bob Menzies had never been called that before.

The two police officers came around and walked slowly up to me.

'You right, sir?' said one, an older man who looked down at me and then around at the old election posters.

I nodded. 'Had a party and...nobody came.'

'Why you got these pictures of underpants in your backyard?'

'It's a party,' I said.

'Fair enough,' he said.

'What you going to do with that fella?'

'It's Bob Menzies, I was going to burn him.'

'Righto.' He looked at me.

I couldn't see the other police officer as he had been scouting the backyard and house. He walked closer to the fire. He held something in his hands. It was Bishe, the Alternatives' big cat. He was to be collected the next week by Andrew's mother.

I looked up at the tall copper with the cat. He was tall.

'How's your freckles?' I asked him.

The older policeman looked at me.

'What did you say, mate?'

'His freckles,' I repeated.

The tall cop laughed.

'Good, good. They're still there.'

He turned to the older cop. 'I got freckles on my shoulders and nowhere else.'

'You know this bloke?' the older cop said.

'Well, yeah.'

'Well I know about his freckles.'

There was a silence. Then we all laughed.

The old cop looked down at me.

'Nobody turned up to your do, eh? That's an old telly.'

'It was the shower,' said the tall cop.

'Eh?'

'The temperature of the shower, why I've got freckles up there. Only thing I can think of.'

The older cop nodded.

'You poor sad desolate prick,' he said in an almost kind tone. I didn't know whether he was talking to me or his mate.

'Want some prawns?'

We sat in front of the telly eating prawns. Howard came on to concede.

We watched him concede. The tall cop fed some prawns to Bishe.

'Andrew was a good bloke,' he said.

I nodded.

'This fella,' said the older cop. 'This fella will be back. Something about him. Like he's got extra batteries up his arse.'

Howard finished his speech and there were cheers. Richard Carleton said that soon Bob Hawke would speak.

The older cop got up.

'Bugger that. Turn it down, don't burn the fence and don't burn Bob Menzies...'

He walked off and the tall cop stroked Bishe one last time and followed his partner.

As they were leaving the older cop laughed. 'I got a pair of them undies for Christmas once.'

There on the television with the flame behind waved Howard bravely. There was something about him but I didn't know what. I held Bob Menzies close and closed my eyes.

# 6

'I always tell the people who are shit!' said Axel. 'And you... you are not shit, you are something else I do not know, but you are not shit. You can have the room.'

This was good. I had graduated from drama school and had spent a few months sleeping on various couches and in beds belonging to others in and around Sydney. The economic miracle of the 1980s was turning slightly sour and finding a room in Bondi was a bit of a bonus all around.

It hadn't been much of an interview.

I had knocked on the door of a flat not far from Bondi Road and waited.

I could hear a shouted conversation, which sounded like an argument, followed by a hissed whispering, which was an argument. I thought they were arguing in German.

When the door opened my suspicions were confirmed.

It was an argument and it was in German.

A tall man stood before me, yelled and held up his hand like a traffic cop.

Then he shut the door. Slamming it in my face.

There was some more shouting, then a silence and the door opened – and there were Axel and his girlfriend, Agnetha, smiling.

I was invited in.

'Tea?' shouted Axel.

I nodded my thanks.

We sat at a small table and drank something that I think was 'herbal'. We said nothing for about fifteen minutes, until Axel pronounced his opinion of me.

'You are not shit! You can have the room.'

I nodded and we shook hands. Then he nodded and we shook hands a little longer. Then he made a sound like the presenters on *Play School* do when they blow out their lips and pretend to be a horse. He took back his hand, waved it at me and yelled, 'Enough!'

And so I was Axel's new housemate. Or rather Axel and his girlfriend's new flatmate.

'That is good you are here.' She smiled.

I nodded back.

'Now I don't have to listen at Axel yelling at people.'

'How many did he yell at?'

'Forty-two.'

'Forty-three if you count that idiot father of the girl who sneezed,' Axel yelled.

'Yes, forty-three. Yes, it is good you are here.'

He was tall, thin, tanned and Teutonic. A German architect on a working visa in Australia. She was also tall, tanned and slightly less Teutonic with a light-eyed European elegance about her, which could also be taken for gormlessness if you were in a particular mood.

She fancied herself as a model, which was handy because it meant their paths sometimes crossed.

He worked for a company that built shopping malls and his specialty was designing the food hall seating in those vast sprawling centres of consumption.

'I sit and make hard plastic seats for all the fat arses who sit and eat the rubbish from the bain-maries. That is what I do.'

He would spend hours walking through shopping centres and food halls looking at seats, and also at the fat arses. She would also spend hours in the same shopping malls working as a model.

Just down the way from the food halls Axel was haunting, his girlfriend would walk up and down a catwalk made from trestle tables and covered with ribbons and cloth.

'All the fat arses go look at the skinny arses and then go eat more rubbish. It's true.'

I nodded. He Playschooled and grew louder.

'It is true! You see, some man in some office worked out his equation, the fat arse – skinny arse equation, and a man like me, the architect, implemented the scheme! All for cash. It's crazy...but it makes money. They will be everywhere these malls. It's all money.' He checked himself and pointed at me. 'You have the rent!'

'I have the rent,' I said.

He eyed me for a moment and nodded his head. 'You always seem to have the rent...what sort of an actor are you?' Then he Playschooled and waved at me.

He was always slightly suspicious that I wouldn't be able to come up with the rent and would provide helpful suggestions about how I could find the money. Mostly they stemmed from his work in the shopping malls of suburban Sydney.

I could, he suggested, sell vegetable slicers, magic mops or portable rubber devices that could transform a household bath into a luxurious spa.

'The people selling these implements are crap, no good. You, I think, might be better. You are an actor.'

'Well, only sometimes.' I smiled.

Axel stared at me.

'It was a joke,' I attempted to explain.

'Rent is no joke,' was all he said. And then he Playschooled.

We didn't see that much of each other, usually only at either end of the day. But they were memorable catch-ups in the kitchen, which is where Axel did his yoga or whatever it was that contorted his limbs into all manner of knots. I had seen some strange sights during my journey through human movement, from Tai Chi Dave to my father trying to start his fleet of mowers, but none held anything to Axel. The first time I saw him, I screamed. He looked at me from around one of his buttocks and Playschooled, although this time he didn't wave.

After a while, when I'd convinced myself he wasn't in the process of some fit, I sat down at the table and ate my breakfast.

'Tell me,' he grunted as he shifted a leg even further along his scalp. 'Tell me about this man with the hair. Hawke.'

I don't know how long Axel had been in Australia, but I knew that he had come by way of Indonesia and Bali. His knowledge of Australia wasn't vast and, for some reason, he seemed to think of me as the first and only port of call on all things Australian. He talked to himself so much though that I was never sure whether or not he was talking to me. I only answered him when he yelled. And, as it happened, that was about every three and a half seconds. He made my father look like a mime.

So of course I didn't look up from my bowl when he muttered the question about Hawke. It was only when he yelled out in a strangled cry that I paid any attention and, for a fleeting moment, I thought he had hurt himself, but he Playschooled and I tried to answer him.

Bob Hawke fascinated him. 'Why does he cry?'

He cried because he was upset about his daughter and he cried because he was upset about being unfaithful to his wife.

'Yes, but why cry in public? On the television.'

I said I didn't know.

'You must know...he is your leader.'

I supposed he cried because he'd lived his life on a wide canvas. Or at least thought he did. Showing his emotions gave his life and prime ministership a certain soap opera quality, an added drama that made him more of a pop star than your usual politician.

The Hawke government had been effective but now the tide had turned and it became clear that Australia was locked between the vagaries of an open world economy and the hangovers from our regulated past; a crunch was coming.

I thought this but just shrugged at Axel. How much did any leader really represent their country? How much did one person reflect the nature of a people?

Axel gave up on Hawke and then started with Rugby League.

'What is the idea? Why does the American black woman sing for them?'

He was speaking about Tina Turner. Advertisements featuring her singing 'Simply the Best' had been flooding television screens.

'Well they're trying to sell the game, Axel.'

'Who to? America?' He Playschooled. 'There is no point, they have their own stupid football.'

'Well they're selling it to…' I didn't know who they were selling it to. 'They are selling it to…more of us.'

'Why don't they have a black Australian singing the song? Do you have such people?' He crossed his legs over his neck and sat looking at me.

'Well, yes, but I don't know whether that would make more people watch the game. Or buy more stuff. Maybe that's the point.'

Axel grunted, uncrossed his legs and got up. 'Young countries.' He sniffed. 'You make mistakes. It is not even a good song. All these man with no necks staring at the old black American with a wig. You think it sells things.'

I didn't say anything. I thought of how often people from other nations were used to sell us something, to really stress its importance. When Bob Hawke wanted to look prime ministerial during an election campaign he would be seen walking through the Rose Garden with Ronald Reagan and then George Bush Snr at the White House. This identified him as being a world leader, being world class.

Axel looked out the back window to the TAFE art school that backed onto the flats.

'You could model. I see some of the life models they use. They should model more for the fat-arse chair I am to design. Perhaps you could do this?'

'How do you see the models?'

'With my eyes! How do you think? I stand on the table and see them.'

'Yes, he does, sometimes with a towel on his head to hide,' said Agnetha.

'You have a bit of a perv do you, Axel?'

I don't think he quite understood.

'Yes, I like to perv,' he said.

'He likes to draw the models but does not want to pay,' said Agnetha.

'That's why I perv, you should give your name.'

I nodded, maybe I could. It certainly seemed worth a thought for the work could hardly be strenuous and it was just over the fence. So I put my name down at the office the next day as a fill-in model.

Around mid year I received a call from the art school asking whether I could fill in for Lois who was off for three weeks.

The night I fronted the classes, pro-democratic protests broke out in Tiananmen Square in China.

I turned up to the studio at the appointed time and was introduced as the model by a teacher who smoked a pipe and wore pens tucked into his long socks.

'Lois is off for three weeks with some study and so we have Michael to pose for us.' I didn't correct him for I was a little nonplussed to see three or four older gentlemen sigh, shake their heads and begin to pack up their gear.

'Now I know it's not ideal,' said Mister Pen-in-socks, 'but we can just do a quick study over a few nights. If you could just disrobe and assume a pose on the platform, thank you, Michael. Something classical would be nice.'

It was cold and, as I started to take my clothes off, I asked innocently, 'Can I leave my slippers on?'

They were a few sighs and the teacher nodded.

'Of course.'

It may not have been strenuous work but it was certainly a little humiliating as I stood starkers in my tartan slippers – especially when I noticed that after assuming a pose I took to be 'classical' (I tried replicating a discus-throwing pose I saw on the wall) another three or four people packed up and humphed out.

'Really, I think you'll find there isn't much difference between what we did with Lois and with Michael,' said the teacher.

I looked at him and he quietly said through his pipe, 'Still please, Michael, *still*!'

So I stood, twisted and starkers, for an hour as the class drew.

After a while I just zoned out and listened to bits and pieces of the conversation that drifted up from the room.

'Those people in the square, who would have thought,' said one woman in the middle of the room.

'Yes, terribly brave, but really I suppose completely pointless in the end…still, Michael, still please,' said Mr Pen-in-socks.

'Why do you think that?'

'Well, I suppose they'll just be dragged off and shot somewhere.'

'What is it they wanted?' This was said by a woman I recognised from a chicken shop in Bondi Road. She was Polish and there was a picture of the British royal family on the wall of her shop. I would go there quite often and get chips.

'With chicken salt, darling?' she would say.

I would nod. I didn't know what chicken salt was, for a while I supposed it was a Polish herb, but the chips were nice.

As she sprinkled I asked why she had a picture of the royal family on her wall.

'I grew up in Poland. Warsaw. I would walk to the British embassy and look at the pictures posted to the gates. They meant a lot, you know. They were wonderful glamour and freedom and the West. They gave me hope, I think they are wonderful.'

I took the chips with chicken salt and looked at the picture. A family with all those ears and teeth and lumps and bumps. Glamour. And freedom.

Back in the art studio, I wondered why she asked what the students wanted in the square. I thought she would know.

'Well, I suppose they wanted freedom, like the people in Russia wanted. They want what we have.'

'Sad really.'

'But how about the fellow with the rags in front of the tanks?'

'Oh, wasn't he brave? They'll get him for sure, he'll be dead.'

'That would make a marvellous painting.'

'Yes...yes...wonderful image.'

They were speaking about the lone demonstrator who had stood in front of a column of tanks brought in to crush the protest. He flagged them down and repeatedly asked the crew of the tank, 'What are you doing here?'

His image was flashed around the world, on the front pages and television screens. He was dubbed the 'Unknown Rebel' and it was as if his courage had validated our political system and the essential rightness of our way of life.

Through the window I saw something waving on the fence. It was a clump of humanity and I assumed it was Axel. I waved back.

'Please, Michael, still. The point is to remain still.'

They were just people in a room, looking at some nude guy in slippers. It was their hobby. They were as far away from Tiananmen Square as you could get.

At the end of the two hours I unwound myself and took the cash that was proffered by Mr Pen-in-socks.

'Thanks, Michael, not bad. But you must remain still... you can put your clothes on now if you like.'

I looked at a few of the students' efforts. One old man smiled and showed me his drawing. A stick figure with big feet. He almost winked. I felt sorry for Lois more than myself.

Axel's effort was even more interesting.

'I was not waving to you,' he said crossly when I walked in.

'Agnetha was bringing me a drink. You should keep still. It is hard to get the likeness.'

'Can I have a look at what you did?'

He Playschooled and waved me away.

'No... but you... you look like a young Elvis Presley... when he was all puppy fat.'

I thought about that for a moment and decided that I needn't see what he had drawn because his description of my slipper-feeted, discus-throwing, podgy Elvis was enough in itself.

•

147

The next week nobody spoke protests and wonderful images. There had been a memorial for the students of the Tiananmen protest and Bob Hawke had read an account of what had happened when the tanks came into the square, which moved him to tears and beyond. Somehow he became the story. A great line of snotty emotion dripped from his nose. It wasn't that it wasn't real. It was messy.

So that's all that the class spoke about. Even the chicken-salt lady.

Another week and it was the cricket. The most unbelievable thing of all was happening on the other side of the world. We were winning the test cricket in England.

The stick figure still wore slippers but this time the old man had added a very healthy and flattering interpretation of an appendage. And this time he added a wink.

'You like it? I do.'

I looked at him.

'How good is the cricket?' I said.

'Marvellous,' he said, 'marvellous. That ball Hughes bowled Broad with was a beauty. How about Mark Taylor? Good eye, he's a surveyor you know. From Wagga, got an uncle from Wagga. Like to think I've got a good eye.'

He may have been an old perv, or maybe he was just an enthusiast who couldn't draw, but whoever he was he could be made bearable with the lingo of cricket.

It took four matches and it seemed Australia had been world beaters for a decade.

When they won the Ashes I sat drinking late at night with Axel.

He stared at the television as I grew more delirious as the Australian team drew closer to victory.

'What is the point?'

'The point is that we are going to win!'

Axel looked at me.

'They all look like fat arses. These are the men of the woman who eat on my chairs. And why do they wear these moustaches?'

'Who cares… We are winning.'

Axel said softly, 'Young countries.'

I rang a friend and we went to celebrate the victory with a horde of happy islanders at the Bondi Hotel.

My friend banged on about the Australian openers.

'There is something about Mark Taylor and Geoff Marsh, you know, they look like they've stepped right out of the fifties. Fantastic. Really solid,' said my friend.

It was the first time I can remember anybody of my vintage starting to look fondly back at the fifties.

A big Maori smiled at us. 'You fellas goin' back to your glory days? Nice white guys winning the cricket.' He laughed.

'Could be your last hurrah, hey? Fifty years time this place will be the colour of all sorts, mate, eh? Be like Brazil. Make the most of those fat white guys!' He rolled off.

I felt a tap on my shoulder.

'I thought it was you by the way you were standing!'

I looked at the man in a cardigan. He seemed vaguely familiar.

He smiled slightly, tilted his head to one side and wiggled it a bit. He introduced himself to me and my friend. 'I'm Nigel. Met Michael at a life art class. Though he's a bit more formal here, aren't you, Mike?'

We had a few more drinks and some strained attempts at conversation about the cricket. Nigel suggested that it might be a good idea if I tried to emulate a square-cut from Tubby Taylor at the next life art class.

'You could lay back, cut loose and open yourself up. Balance on the back foot. For a chubby bub he's surprisingly elegant. Be a fantastic form to try and capture.'

I went red.

'Great idea, Mikey!' my friend laughed.

I never spoke with Nigel again, although whenever I watched Mark Taylor play his trademark back-foot cut I became fidgety and rather uncomfortable. Somewhere out there was Nigel in his blue cardigan with paper and pencil scribbling down a nude study of the Australian cricket captain.

After a while, and a few more drinks, I made my way home up Bondi Road. It was late. The royal family's favourite chicken shop was shut, so I went to the servo across from where I lived. A Chinese man served behind the counter on the all-night shift. I'd seen him often enough when I went to buy a microwaved beef or chicken roll late at night.

It was four in the morning and I'd put a chicken roll in the oven. I couldn't be bothered flipping through the magazines in front of the counter, so I spoke to the man instead.

I asked him about the hours. About the job.

'It terrible. I get so tired. It terrible.'

'You got any other work?'

'Researcher at the university.'

'Oh...'

'Research at... research project...' He blinked. 'Um... I do... physics.'

'Physics...' I repeated. 'Gee...you must be buggered.'

He stared at me.

'Tired...you must be tired.'

'I feel terrible. It so cold.'

'Yes. It is... Cold. How long you done?' I went to lean on the counter and slipped. 'It's all right, all right. Sorry... How long you done?' I waved my hand around the shop.

He looked at me and then down at the grease mark my hand had left on the laminex of the counter.

'Three nights a week... I work here for three months.'

'Really.'

Working in the twenty-four-hour servo. Serving bleary eyed people fast food, bad-tempered drivers cigarettes and cans of Coke to keep them from falling asleep. A physicist working the all-night shift.

'How long do you think you'll last?'

'Seven month...seven month and then I finish project and go home.'

'Where is that... China?' It was late.

'Yes, China.'

'Is that the proper China or the other funny little one...the one where they make the Kmart shoes?'

He blinked. 'You'd be from the big one then would you? The big China?'

It was very late.

'Beijing!' he shouted.

'Beijing, right.'

Before I could ask him about my chicken roll he shouted again. 'Tiananmen Square... Oh terrible, terrible. Just terrible.'

The microwave tinged ready but he still looked at me.

'Worried about going home… to… China?'

'No. No.' He reached down and wiped away the mark my hand had left. 'Because soon in years all the old men die. All be gone. Then they'll be democracy.' He held up the Chux towel like a flag and smiled.

'You really think so?'

'Of course. Of course. Of course.'

We stared at each other. I wanted my roll and I suddenly felt like getting a chocolate. A Pollywaffle. I opened my mouth to order.

'I know what you say.' He pointed to stop me from talking. 'Dangerous, but I go home. Must go. All my family there – I miss them. My nephew was a student. He was at the square, don't know what happened… so I must go home.' He put away the towel. 'When I get tired here I fall asleep and think of home. It's no good – I think of my nephew and family.'

He smiled and blinked.

'Yes… could I have my roll please?'

He pointed out to the petrol bowsers under the fluorescent lights. 'I go outside then. The cold, it makes me awake. It's so cold it takes away my sleep and I don't think of my nephew – so the cold is good for that. For forgetting.'

'Can I have my roll?'

He wasn't listening. 'But if I forget, I can't see him or my family. I can't see them in the square. I don't know…' He looked at me. 'Is it bad to forget?… I get so tired.'

'Mate, can I have my roll?'

He looked at me and then nodded. He took the roll out of the microwave and held it as it steamed.

'These.' He proffered the roll. 'These are not good… for you.'

'Just give me my roll, mate.'

He handed it across to me and nodded.

'All the old men and my nephew,' he said.

I nodded and walked out. I took a bite of the roll. It was hot and not much else. It tasted of nothing. I walked on and then stopped. I'd forgotten my Pollywaffle.

I turned around and saw the man from behind the counter standing under the bright lights by the petrol bowsers. He held his head with one hand and looked tired. It was cold. I thought about my Pollywaffle. I'd forgotten it. The cold makes you forget. I walked home.

Bob Hawke went from tears to laughter and receptions at the Lodge. Allan Border, the Australian cricket captain, came back to a ticker-tape parade and tossing the coin at football grand finals, and ended up Australian of the Year.

At the Rugby League grand final Mal Meninga, the winning Canberra captain, lifted the cup and declared that his Canberra Raiders team was, 'Just like the federal Labor government – we just keep on winning.'

Bob Hawke had the grace to look surprised and grateful. And well he might for things were going well for Bob – the Leader of the Opposition, John Howard, had been replaced by Andrew Peacock because Howard was thought to be unelectable.

Why anybody would vote for Andrew Peacock is lost in the mists of time. The problem wasn't that he was untalented or inept, but he looked and behaved like he was somebody who was pretending to be a politician. He even sounded like he was an old actor with his super-serious voice and grave, straight-browed manner. He was, put simply, a man whose time had passed and the great irony was that the time of the man who he had replaced had yet to come.

Bob Hawke was still gaining a great deal of worth from his association with sport, and the success of the Australian cricket team validated his prime ministership even further.

The economy though was a beast that was becoming an even more unsteady mount and I once again turned to one of Axel's suggestions to find a source of income.

'Do not be ashamed. It is acting. If what she does is modelling,' said Axel pointing towards Agnetha, 'then what you will be doing is acting. Sure!' And, true to form, he Playschooled.

I have a confession. I have belonged to a vast and silent army of men who have forsaken their own identity for the benefit of mankind. An army of highly trained men from many nations who have worn one uniform. No, not the French Foreign Legion, for this army of mercenaries has seen action more dangerous and bloodcurdling than even the most hardened Legionnaire. I have served as Santa Claus.

It had started over a beer, as most great adventures do, with a friend of mine from drama school. He had a job he couldn't make and asked if I was up for it. Like a fool I said yes and an hour later I found myself sitting in the only uncovered part of a Perth shopping centre on the hottest day of the year.

Sitting in a sleigh dressed in the Santa suit which had been provided for my friend. This friend was two feet shorter than me.

'It'll be fascinatin', fascinatin',' he assured me.

I just managed to squeeze my limbs into the suit. The boots were hopeless, so I wore my thongs. I was given a small bell to ring, a bag of lollies to distribute and was let loose. Unfortunately, the heat was too much and I promptly fell asleep.

Nobody seemed to notice. Anyone who was vaguely interested probably took me to be a pretty ordinary Christmas decoration.

When I woke three hours later my feet and nose were blistered and redder than my suit. My throat was parched and when I tried to speak to collect my pay I sounded like a dying cat.

But I had form and my career began to look up with Axel's help. He had been talking to a store manager on one of his food court trips.

'It is Christmas and they need the Kringle man!'

Things looked up for my next outing as I was moving to the big league – a Santa in one of the nation's 'better department stores'.

One particular store had found itself a Santa down after an unfortunate incident with a tired and emotional Kris Kringle in the sporting goods department. He was found pissed as a newt under some golf clubs.

I was given the job after a brief and rather strained interview. The person interviewing me was called Kaylee. She looked about twelve and kept marking and colouring in notes on a pad with different coloured textas. She spoke with a shrill, staccato yell, as if she was communicating with a profoundly deaf alien, or better still like one of those characters in an old movie who speaks slowly and patronisingly to a group of natives. 'What…makes…you…think…you…have…got…what… it…takes…to…be…one…of the…nation's…better… department…stores'… Santy?'

I thought I'd reply in kind, just as a joke. 'Me...be...good... Santy... Claus...' I beat my chest. 'Because...me...believem in... Santy Claus.'

There was a silence that stretched quite a bit longer than I thought was possible. She thought I was serious. She picked up a phone and said very clearly and loudly, 'He...was... the...only...one, wasn't...he? You...are...sure?'

She hung up the phone and screamed, 'Congratulations, you...are our...new... Santy... Claus.'

I was given a baggy red suit, a beard that smelt of sherry and a mentor Santa – a man called Ernie. He had a stutter, a gammy leg and a scar that stretched across his forehead thanks to his time in Korea, 'during the emergency'. He was Yoda to my Luke Skywalker.

Ernie tutored me in the ways of the Kringle – the protocol and etiquette. And what protocol and etiquette. Santas were never allowed to talk religion or politics. Not being able to talk religion at Christmas time seemed to be a reasonable illustration of how far the whole event has been removed from any spiritual significance. 'Don't ever mention J-j-j-j-esus if you can help it, sport,' advised Ernie. 'It just mixes up a lot of the New A-australians.'

Kaylee was a little bit more diplomatic. 'It...is... Christmas... So...we...don't...want to...up...set... anybody.'

Santas from 'one of Australia's better department stores' were allowed to direct parents seeking Christmas ideas to Santa's Gift Idea Ledger. This was the latest catalogue bound in a smelly red vinyl cover that stood on a polystyrene foam tree stump that had seen better days. Christmas was fraying around the edges.

It looked even more frayed because we had entered the beginnings of the recession we had to have. Depending on who you spoke to, the tightening of interest rates and the slowing of growth was responsible for firewalling the economy and readjusting the fundamental settings to make Australia a truly open system, which could more effectively ride the tide of the world economy; or it was just, in Ernie's terms, 'P-p-p-p-eople buggering ar-r-r-round.'

Bob Hawke began to look a little tatty and a little worried despite all of Paul Keating's salesman-like spruiking of the recession.

But there were far more important issues at hand.

Santa, or Santy as Kaylee insisted on calling me, had to know the names of Santa's reindeer.

For thirty minutes I sat in front of Ernie as he tried to recite the reindeer names. Having a man with a chronic stutter go through the reindeer names is something I never wish to go through again. At the end of the allotted time I was really no wiser, Ernie barely getting to the first two names and the rest sounding like an old distress signal signed in Morse code from some rapidly sinking steamship. The more frustrated Ernie got, the more frenetic his Morse-code message. I was lost with all hands.

I was introduced to Sharon, Santa's helper, whose job it was to take the photographs of Santa and his happy kiddie friends. She was a large, rather mournful girl with sad eyes, but she had a lovely smile.

Before I was to embark on my first Santa mission, Ernie pulled me aside and dispensed some wise advice. 'Watch for the over enthusiastic k-k-k-kiddies. They can get ya in an uninin-in-intentional e-e-e-em-m-mmotional death g-g-g-grip.' Ernie was kind enough to show a little 'ju-ju-ju-jitsu trick' taught to him by a sergeant in the Black Watch in Korea, to combat over-affectionate little ones.

He almost broke my thumb with some crazed grabbling manoeuvre and when, quite naturally, I tried to take my thumb back his left fist came with it, rather fast. He hit me flush on the jaw. My first day on the job and I was knocked to the ground by a stuttering seventy-year-old with a gammy leg.

Ernie helped me up, compounding my shame. 'S-S-S-Sorrry, sport, an aut-t-t-t-omatic reaction. And these k-k-k-kiddies can move like l-l-l-l-l-lightning. Watch yourself.'

Thus armed and warned I took my place on Santa's throne in Santa's workshop.

The throne was fine but the workshop was in the middle of the lingerie department, which seemed a bit odd. Sharon explained that the lingerie department was popular with mothers and they would purchase goods while waiting for their children. So the spirit of Christmas sounded not so much like 'Jingle Bells' but 'Jingle Tills'.

Undeterred, I took my place on the throne and Ho-ho'd my head off amongst bras, teddies and panties. At first there was nobody there so I bellowed even louder. Sharon pursed her lips and signalled me to calm down a bit. 'We don' want that weird girl who screams at you down here,' she whispered, 'stop sounding like a bull in rut.'

Suitably advised I calmed down and, soon enough, a procession of children greeted me. It is somewhat humbling to think that somewhere in some photo album I sit with these children. Few smiled. Some were bored. Most were simply terrified. The poor things had no idea who this bellowing, red-suited loon really was. Santa might sound all right as a friendly fellow who pops down the chimney at night, but a real-life version can be slightly traumatising.

I never had to use dear old Ernie's jujitsu hold, but I did need sponges and towels to protect myself from nervous little bowels.

I never really understood why some parents forced the issue. One father kept barking at his twins to stop 'whining and start smiling, I'm payin' money for this and your nanna's going to want it.' Consequently the image is of two little boys with frozen smiles of terror, probably peering out from Nanna's sideboard.

Another time a little Pakistani boy was placed on my knee and commenced howling, screaming and tearing at my beard. While I tried to keep his fingers from my throat and eyes his parents looked on smilingly. 'For the folks back home!' said the father. God knows what the folks made of the way we in the Christian West celebrated Christmas, but I hoped Kaylee informed him the whole ritual had nothing to with religion or politics.

One highlight of my time on the throne was when my future wife came to visit me. She had already proved her love by buying me a pair of gumboots so I could actually do the job and now she wanted to see her investment at work.

Seeing her, I leapt from my throne and ran towards her, ringing my bell and bellowing my ho-hos. Like any sane person, she took off and, like any dedicated Santa, I pursued my quarry.

Unfortunately, in my haste, I unwittingly collected a few of Berlei's best sports bras in my outfit and took off looking like some macabre spectre from the Mardi Gras.

My quarry was stopped by store security and asked if 'that Santa is bothering you?'

My future intended, of course, replied that she was being stalked by some rogue Kringle. I was led off shedding bras and protesting my innocence and had to spend a while being lectured by Kaylee on more 'Santy' protocol.

She noted that there had been complaints about my inability to name all of Santy's reindeers. I couldn't protest this, I had no idea. She asked me to name them. The first two were all I could decipher from Ernie's gibbering. After that I was on my own. They came in pairs. 'Donner and Blitzen... Donner and Blitzen... Gott and Himmell... Trevor and Reg... Martin and Lewis... Wentworth, Blaxland and Lawson.' I stopped, waiting. To my amazement I wasn't given the sack. 'Well...at...least... you...have...been...doing...your...homework!' yelled Kaylee. I wasn't the only person who didn't understand Ernie.

I was, however, put on notice. Kaylee would be keeping a close eye on me. I tried to behave, but it was hard. At times it was incredibly, mind-numbingly boring.

I'd spend hours sitting on the throne listening to the muzak pumped out over the store's sound system like some toxic waste seeping into your mind. At the same time there were moments of high surrealism. While sitting in my kingdom, dozing away, from nowhere emerged a platoon of large American marines. They moved through the undies and night apparel as if they were on reconnaissance patrol. They were all armed, with helmets and combat paint. They said nothing, save for a huge bull-necked man. 'Merry Christmas, Santa,' he rumbled as he went by.

God knows what they were doing there, especially in the lingerie, but I'm sure it was all part of someone's grand plan.

There was also the day that Ernie's bad leg spasmed and I had to help him from the throne to the medical room.

Shoppers were treated to the sight of two Santas apparently engaging in some lewd mauling mating ritual to the strains of Andy Williams singing 'Winter Wonderland'.

I barely got to know the people I worked with. Ernie was simply too scary, especially when he invited me to go bushwalking with him. Sharon would sometimes arrive at work teary eyed and distracted.

I asked one day if she was all right and she burst into tears. I took her into Santa's Cave so she could get herself together. She was, she sobbed, late. A week late. I tried to digest this and then, well, it must have been the whole Christmas thing because I realised she was pregnant.

'Have you told anyone?' I asked in what I hoped was a sympathetic tone.

'My parents,' she sniffed. 'And they nearly killed me.'

'What about your boyfriend... You have a partner...a boyfriend?' My beard was getting stuck in my teeth.

Sharon blinked a bit and sniffed. 'He couldn't care less. Your beard is going in your mouth.'

I was gallant. 'Don't worry about me. What about you? Is there anyone you can talk to? I mean really talk to?'

Sharon looked at me closer.

I didn't think I was being clear. 'You know,' I said, nodding my head. 'About being...you know...late.'

Sharon looked for a bit longer. Then she snarled, 'You fucking tool. You think I'm up the duff? I forgot to put me dole form in. You tool. I'll get cut off. You think I'm up the duff? You tool.'

I tried to say sorry but more of my beard was in my mouth than I realised. I coughed. I coughed again. Kaylee had come down to our floor. I coughed so loud as we left Santa's Cave that she asked me if I was all right.

Sharon supplied the answer. 'He's not right in the head. He thinks I'm pregnant.' I coughed and pulled what seemed like a metre of beard from my throat.

Kaylee stared at me and Sharon. This was too much. I could see her mind working, so I just bellowed at her, 'HO! HO! HO!' She got such a fright she took off for her office upstairs.

Sharon looked at me. 'You're off your head. You tool.'

Amid all this chaos something happened that I will never forget.

A family came to have their Christmas photo taken. Mum and Dad and four children. Only one, a little boy, was dressed in his Sunday best. The other children looked like they had been interrupted mid sandpit-fight. Spoilt kid, I thought. Has to have his photo taken. Mum looked on as the little boy approached, she was red-eyed and haggard.

'Come on,' I cried in Santa mode, 'bring your brother and sisters up.'

The father smiled tightly and shook his head. 'Too expensive, Santa.'

I nodded and noticed the little boy on my lap had bandages on his elbows. 'Come off your skateboard, matey?' I roared.

The little boy looked to his mother and she started to cry. Then he whispered to me. 'I've got leukaemia, Santa.'

I continued my routine. Did he have any wishes? To his mum he said he wanted a toy jeep. She smiled and said she'd see. His little hand took mine and he whispered to me again. 'I know you're only pretend, I know, but I wish Mummy wasn't so sad. I wish she was happy.'

I watched them walk off through the store, swallowed by the tinsel, the children's voices drowned out by some tortured Christmas carol on the speaker system.

I looked after them for sometime.

A little while later, I received a visit from a familiar face. It was Axel. He'd been wandering through the shopping centre.

'You are the third Santa man I have spoken to,' he said without much emotion.

'Well, come on then, come up here and tell Santa what you would like for Christmas.' I ho-ho'd.

Amazingly Axel put down his satchel and sat on my lap. He did so straight-faced and completely devoid of any humour.

He had stopped by to tell me that he and Agnetha were splitting up. She wanted to stay and he wanted to move on.

'She wants to have the residency. So she will marry a friend of ours. She must live with him and I... I want to go to the Bali again.'

'Well, I am sorry.'

He Playschooled and shouted, 'Enough!'

A few heads turned. And they were followed by even more when he went on.

'You must leave the flat. I must leave the flat. Can you help me pack up?'

I nodded my beard and asked him if he was all right.

'Sure. Sure. I just feel old.'

•

We packed things up and Agnetha waved goodbye from a caramel Hunter driven by a red-haired engineer who was to become her husband.

'She wasn't really ever a very good model. Walking up and down for the fat arses, but she was nice,' said Axel as we stood in the street. And then he Playschooled and added, 'I'm hungry.'

We walked down to the Polish lady's chicken shop and sat outside eating chips.

A father and son walked past. They were Orthodox Jews. There were many in Bondi. The father wore a trilby hat and had a beard. The boy looked very pale and younger than he probably was. He wore a yarmulke. They were both dressed in black trousers and white shirts.

Axel looked up with a chip in his mouth and looked after them for a while then let out a long sigh.

'You are lucky, puppy-fat Elvis. You come from a young country. It must be good not to have to live with your past. To have no history.'

I never saw him again.

A few days later I got tired of going in to Santy's Workshop. I'm sure Ernie manfully carried on, and I'm sure somebody somewhere would have been found to fill my boots and padded suit.

But even today when I walk through the shops at Christmas time and it all seems too much, the commercialism, the noise, the sales, the Santas on every corner, I think of that little boy. And of his love for his mum. And I think of Axel and how he thought I and Australia were lucky. Lucky not to live with our past. How many Australians thought that? How many still do?

Bob Hawke was conveniently forgetting his past or, more accurately, forgetting about what had been agreed to in his past.

Labor won another federal election during which the environment was used to great effect by Senator Graham Richardson for the Labor Party. Suddenly a numbers man from the New South Wales right found a bush track to Damascus and the ALP ads featured lots of big trees crashing to the ground. This time nobody mentioned children living in poverty and bringing people together, it was just lots of finger pointing and seat-by-seat targeting. A green whisper campaign against the dandy Andy and his pinstriped retinue.

Andrew Peacock's demeanour never, ever changed, even as he lost. He must have been deeply hurt but he kept his measured tone and serious brow right up until the end. It seemed he was more like a character from some ghastly soap opera than any real person, but he always maintained a civility that seemed to have vanished completely from public life. Peacock's promise threatened more than it ever achieved.

'Well at least he's always polite,' said my mother, 'even if he does look like he's always about to do a Stewart Granger impersonation.'

Stewart Granger was an old, oily charmed matinee idol from the 1940s and 1950s who specialised in the creative force of the eyebrow.

But it was Bob Hawke who took the whole business of soap opera politics to a new height after he fell out with his treasurer Paul Keating.

After he had done away with Andrew Peacock/Stewart Granger Hawke was supposed to step down and let Paul Keating have a crack at the top job. The infamous Kirribilli Agreement probably wasn't the first such commitment made, and certainly won't be the last broken, but the fact that it became public made the whole affair look more like somebody having a dummy-spit because they didn't get a chance to open the batting in a club match after they were promised.

It was small town in its feel and the analogy between sport – with its in-fighting and moaning – and public life was never more apparent.

Bob Hawke raised the idolisation of sport and its caressing of the public's pride because he genuinely believed it himself. That's what made him such a recognisable and welcomed type.

The fact that Paul Keating attempted to follow was testament to how much he wanted the job of prime minister. When Collingwood won the AFL grand final in 1990 Paul Keating showed up later in the night as scenes of bacchanalian excess were paraded at the club's home ground, Victoria Park.

Earlier in the evening I was told by an Essendon supporter, the club that Collingwood had beaten in the grand final, that I should go and see how low human beings can fall on the evolutionary scale as the mighty Magpies celebrated their victory.

I took him up on the offer and walked up Smith Street. The scenes didn't disappoint. Although my Essendon friend was drawing a long bow about the potential descent into depravity, I'll admit there were some moments that seemed not too far from a Saturday night Heart of Darkness, but really it was just lots of happy people.

Mob joy. To somebody from another land it might have seemed like a cross between a riot or celebrations of a war ending. The streets were filled with dancing people, and so were the cars. I saw a couple jitterbugging on top of a Silver

Top taxi while the driver sat frozen inside as the car lurched from side to side.

At Victoria Park itself I earned myself a hundred dollars when I climbed a point post on a dare from somebody behind me. The club's theme song was sung over and over again, and late in the night it was sung again by a man with the words written on his hand.

Paul Keating, hailing from Bankstown in Sydney, had taken the chance of a bit of populist vaudeville by becoming a ticket holder at Collingwood.

He climbed the stage and sang the club song. He didn't receive a single boo or sign of uninterest, although an old man in a beanie drinking Melbourne Bitter beside me said loudly, 'That bastard has got the words written on his hand. See how he's holding his hand?'

But he soon went back to his Mel Bitter and Keating went on to the keys of the Lodge.

After the election win Bob Hawke seemed to grow old very quickly. It didn't help that the recession worsened and that unemployment and interest rates rose. He was opposed by a new younger face in Dr John Hewson, an economist who had performed well against Keating in the 1990 election.

Not unsurprisingly, Hawke thought he was still the best man for the job and fell out with his deputy when Keating started making rumbling sounds reminiscent of the 'trash talk' that goes on before boxing matches and football games.

He challenged for the leadership, was beaten and quite happily went off to the backbench to watch Bob Hawke flail against time and John Hewson.

Hawke's fate seemed to match the strangeness of the sporting festivals he presided over. How long ago those days of the America's Cup must have seemed to him in the early spring of 1991.

How things had changed. The heady flag waving was the height of his love affair with the Australian people. Now all he had were afternoons like the Australian Rugby League grand final. I don't know if he saw the same spectacle as I did. His chosen team, the Canberra Raiders, were playing the Penrith Panthers but really the game was secondary to what went before.

I walked through the front doors of the Powell Hotel in Melbourne as Bob Hawke was being shown his seat at the Sydney Football Stadium. It was a Sunday in late September and I had nothing much to do except walk in through those doors and watch the grand final on the big television screens. There was only a handful of people there.

To my surprise the television was already tuned into the game.

'You've got the footy on,' I said to an uninterested looking guy behind the bar.

'No, a Pommy bloke wants to watch the Rugby. Snot the footy.'

I nodded, this was Melbourne after all, there was only one 'footy' in those days. I was about to pull up a chair when an old man sang out, 'You born in a tent? Bloody Arab, close bloody door.' He was spectacularly drunk.

This was a good effort as it was only two o'clock in the afternoon.

I looked at him and another voice rang out.

'Close bluddy door!'

This, I took it, must have been the Pommy bloke. He was round and pale and hairy. He wore a big white T-shirt, shorts and sandals. In the right sort of light he looked a little like Charles Laughton.

I closed the door.

The barman shook his head.

The Pommy bloke looked at me and was about to say something else when he was interrupted by the spectacular drunk. This man, I saw, had a huge head of hair, a big boofy wave of black immaculately combed into a flowing quiff. It must have been dyed to within an inch of its existence because the fellow was very old.

He had that gurgling, slagging quality to his voice that denotes a lifetime of alcohol and tobacco use.

'Here he is. Good old Bob. You poor old prick!'

'Why'd ja feel sorry for 'im? Christ why? He's ruined the bluudy country. Mate, I voted for him!'

'Poor old Bob,' repeated the spectacular drunk and, as I looked at him, I noticed his eyes had disappeared.

His hair had covered them. Then I realised his hair wasn't in fact his, it was a wig. A great head of Elvis hair. He grabbed it with both hands and pushed it up with his palms flat on his temples. His hairline rose and he opened his eyes wide and blinked.

The hair was so big it looked like a busby a grenadier might wear on guard duty outside Buckingham Palace.

'You right?' said Charles Laughton.

'Got a hair in me eye.'

'Give uuuus a luuuke,' said Charles Laughton and he tried to open the eye with his great pork-sausage fingers.

'Ohhh,' gurgled the spectacular drunk.

'Bob Hawke, the Prime Minister of Australia,' said a voice from the television and we saw Bob taking his seat.

'You don't want that bloke, all he does is cry. Call 'im a prime minister? Bloody Churchill wouldn't cry, bloody Thatcher wouldn't cry but he cries at the drop of a hat.'

'What would you know?' said the spectacular drunk.

'You want a beer, mate?' asked the barman.

I nodded.

'What I know is that you'd be nothin' without us. You'd be a bunch of fookin' raggedy natives out in the middle of nowhere.' He wriggled on his chair and scratched at himself. 'Running around with your boomerangs.' Then he laughed and clapped his hands.

'My boomerang won't come back,' he started to sing a novelty song by an English comic from the 1960s called Charlie Drake. It was all about an Aboriginal man who couldn't get his boomerang to come back when he threw it. It was a song as offensive and as cliché-ridden as you could find. It was also a staple of Rugby nights when you were either dressed as a woman or blacked up in Kiwi boot polish miming to the song.

'Jesus, this is what ya give us. Piss orf,' yelled the spectacular drunk. The bar man handed me a beer, sniffed and went back to reading his Sunday paper.

'Piss off out here.' The spectacular drunk started to sing the refrain of 'Waltzing Matilda' over and over as his hair fell down over his eyes.

Charles Laughton kept on singing 'My Boomerang Won't Come Back'.

There was another shot of Bob Hawke squinting into the sun and then there was the pre-game entertainment.

It used to be a game of sport. Now what appeared before us on the screens was something that was about as meaningful as what was occurring in the bar beside me.

It was an international smorgasbord of entertainment. That's what another voice from the television said and so the working man's game was heralded with the most surreal set of images.

First of all the parachutist who had a camera strapped to his leg to broadcast images of his descent to the television network got stuck up on the grandstand roof and was conveniently ignored for the rest of the afternoon.

Then a procession of people dressed as dead rock and roll singers warbled into a microphone on top of a large record on a turntable. There was someone doing a non-puppy-fat Elvis. Charles Laughton stopped singing and yelled to the spectacular drunk, 'That bloke's got your hair!'

Then came Buddy Holly and then a Roy Orbison who sounded more like Smoky Dawson.

'They shall live forever with their music,' intoned a deep booming voice across the Sydney Football Stadium, as if he were doing an audition for Anzac Day.

'And we will remember...here is Roy Orbison and the pretty women of the June Dally-Watkins School of Modelling.'

The man dressed as Roy, who sounded like Smoky Dawson, sang 'Pretty Woman' and from nowhere hundreds of swim-suited models from the suburbs of Sydney wobbled in pink.

'Oh 'ullo,' said Charles Laughton.

'Yeah,' said the spectacular drunk. 'There you go, look at that! You won't see that in Pommy land.'

'And there's a bloody reason for it too...it's just a bloody game there...look at this, you lot can't be trusted, this is what you think is bloody good television...back 'ome we just watch the non-tarted-up sport and then we can watch quality telly... Like *The Good Life*.'

Both the barman and I exchanged looks. He shook his head. I called for a beer.

'Piss orf,' gurgled the spectacular drunk.

A voice boomed again as the pretty women ran back to their suburbs and Roy/Smoky went back to his next pub engagement.

'Young music, the music of the young,' boomed the voice again. This time two former football players stood and recreated a famous pose, which was also celebrated in the trophy the teams were playing for. These two old men stood together until a slightly podgy young blonde woman, complete with a Tom of Finland cap, jiggled up onto the stage beside them after being dropped off by a beard riding a black Harley-Davidson.

Her boots had platforms the size of Centrepoint Tower so she moved rather stiffly.

She started singing about feeling sexy and the two old footballers in their old men's blazers and ties stood awkwardly as fake tanned body builders in tiny fluorescent Speedos posed their swollen bodies in front of some of June Dally-Watkins leftovers.

There was silence in the pub. No more boomerangs not coming back and no more waltzing matildas. We all stared at the screen.

The blonde woman swayed, nearly fell and struck a pose as the feeling sexy song finished.

As the stage cleared Charles Laughton was about to say something but then the finale of the international smorgasbord erupted.

Of all the bits of music to play before a football match I don't think anyone would have ever thought of 'YMCA'. But that's what we got. Complete with the group Village People – a theme group of overtly camp characters supposedly drawn from the surrounds of Greenwich Village in New York.

In front of these happy Yanks, who knew next to nothing about the game they were helping celebrate, skinny blond young men performed callisthenics routines and somersaults dressed in white lycra tights.

Then the voice boomed from the television: 'The national anthem sung by the Phantom of the Opera, Anthony Warlow.'

He had a nice voice and thankfully he sang without a cap and mask.

'Australians all let us rejoice.'

Finally Charles Laughton had had enough.

'This fooking country is beyond belief. I'll give you a bloody show.'

With that he staggered off his chair, took a few paces back, turned around and dropped his shorts to moon the screen.

The spectacular drunk turned to look and his hair slid even further down his face.

A huge white bottom, with two pink spots on the centre of each cheek and two testicles hanging free stared up at the television screen.

For a moment I thought of Axel and of young countries.

There was a moment of quiet and then the barman said, without looking up from his paper, 'I knew I was a republican for a reason.'

Nobody said anything for a long time, save for a gurgle from the Elvis busby-wearing drunk.

'Poor Old Bob. Poor old Bob,' he repeated.

He did look old. And he had to sit through that mad unreal afternoon trying to look prime ministerial.

I can't remember much of the game. I know Bob's team lost. And a little over two months later so did he.

# 7

The 216 from Melbourne bounced and lurched like an old boat down the lumpy asphalt of Dynon Road towards Footscray. Outside, running alongside the railway yards, the skeletons of old industry stood in the dark. A purple light onboard the bus turned the passengers' faces into ghostly hollow-eyed spectres.

The purple lights were to deter people who wanted to hit up.

No sooner had the lights come on than the bus slowed and stopped at an intersection. There were a few panelbeaters and an engineering works beside the road and another building with a red light and a sign with funny old-fashioned writing, like the graphics from a Doris Day sex comedy from the sixties, 'The Tender Touch'. It was a brothel. A few figures stood in its car park and one was walking towards the front door. The Tender Touch – the name sounded like it belonged to an old film in which Doris and Rock Hudson primly flirt with each other.

While the lights of the intersection and the Doris and Rock brothel both hummed red the driver turned away from the wheel and faced us. He was a big islander.

'He's gone. Bob's gone. Just on the news. Keating's the prime minister.' He turned back to face the road and the darkness in front.

Nobody said anything. A few seats away from me a couple sat nodding in the purple night. They were both out of it. She, just barely awake, stared at her partner with heavy eyes, and started tapping him on the shoulder. 'Hey, hey,' she said.

'Hey, hey. Bob Hawke. Bob Hawke,' she said again.

Her partner stirred a little.

'Bob Hawke's not prime minister anymore,' she said.

Her partner finally opened his eyes and looked at her. Or, rather, past her and out at the man walking into the entrance of the Doris and Rock Tender Touch.

'Bob Hawke's not prime minister.'

'That fella's getting a root, look. He's going for a root.'

'Talking about Bob Hawke.'

'Good for him. He's getting some, spending his money.'

'Shit, fuck ya, I'm talking about Bob Hawke.'

Her partner closed his eyes.

'Who he?'

They both fell silent, the traffic lights changed and the 216 lurched off. A few stops later I pulled the cord for my stop.

I walked down the aisle behind an old lady who was getting off as well and we passed the two junkies. They both looked out of it. The woman briefly opened her eyes and looked straight at me. She closed them after a few moments and said softly, 'Go Bombers.'

I kept on walking and thanked the driver with a nod. 'So Keating's got the job.'

The driver nodded.

'Oh well,' I said.

'They forget quick,' the driver said as I turned to the step. 'People forget quick. Don't have to be hammered to forget, eh. We all got it coming to us. All be forgotten.' And he laughed.

The old lady walked ahead of me with a flotilla of shopping bags.

I asked her if she needed a hand. She smiled and said she wouldn't mind. I took the bags and we walked along together. She was heading towards the laundromat which was down the road a bit.

'My neighbour is going to meet me there. She's doing her drying.'

I didn't say anything.

'You have a grandma?' she asked

'I did,' I said, 'but she died years ago when I was little.'

'You have a grandad?'

I shook my head.

'Oh, that's no good. I wish I'd known mine. Well, I do in a way, because I've heard about him and there's a photo of him. But it would have been lovely to feel him.'

I didn't say anything.

'That bus driver, what he said about forgetting. Well, I don't know. I've just had my grandchildren over.'

'Oh yes.'

'Paper everywhere. It was lovely. I taught them how to do cut-outs. My eldest granddaughter made a bride and groom out of the *Age*. Bob Hawke and Paul Keating. You could see bits of their photos from the *Age*. There they were, bride and groom.'

'That sounds like fun.'

'Well, I don't know. I teach them how to lacquer them, they go all hard and you can put your fingers up them. Up Bob and Keating.'

I wished I hadn't stopped to carry the bags, I wanted to go and watch the news reports about the challenge.

'My granddaughter said that she wished she lived closer so she could play more with me. She'd get tired of the sight of me, I bet. That's the way it seems.'

The laundromat wasn't far and I walked a little quicker. Inside, I could see the lights shone bright with that hard fluorescent glare and the walls were covered in photos, hundreds of images of old and not-so-old movie stars. The laundromat was called 'Legends' and I sometimes did my washing there. I could never quite understand why in Droop Street, Footscray, a little shrine to make-believe had been created in a room full of washing machines and dryers. For an actor it was a little ironic to see the posed smiles and images of success plastered above the texta-written '$1 for soap powder' sign. When I washed my undies Humphrey Bogart and Marilyn Monroe would look on in touched-up, pancake made-up immortality.

The old lady smiled as we drew closer to the laundromat and laughed a little at some memory I was sure she was going to share with me, for she was one of those old ladies who loved to tell stories to strangers, and it made me feel a little guilty about being slightly pissed off for helping her.

'You know,' she said, 'when I was little there were these people across the way who used to tie this poor old dog up to a post in the garden and he used to bark and bark and bark, the poor old fellow. And I couldn't do anything; they would have told me to just mind my own business, but he would drive me desperate that old dog.'

We had reached the entrance of the laundromat and above the old lady's head lots of dead movie actors smirked at me.

'So I said to myself, well at least I can hear him and I know I'm alive, and it didn't bother me so much after that. That's what you've got to do when something's worrying you. Change your thinking about it. Change your mind about it and it will go away.'

I looked at her and she smiled her nice old lady smile.

'And the dog just stayed there tied up?'

She nodded. 'Poor old fella. That's the problem. You can change your thinking and you can forget, it's just sometimes you hear the noise of the barking that you remember and you think. I suppose it's what the pollies do, they think differently. That's why they can forget so well. It's a handy trick to have.'

I couldn't see what the point of her story was.

'Hello, here she is.' The old lady smiled at an immense woman in black folding a pile of black clothes.

The huge goth nodded at me and then smiled at the old lady.

'This is Therese, my neighbour,' said the old lady.

I looked at Therese and the old lady.

'I was just helping her…your neighbour.' I felt like I had to explain to Therese.

'That's nice of you, thanks,' said Therese in a voice that I'm sure was more suited to a Terry. In fact it became quite clear that Therese was a Terry. Well, whatever, I'm sure that the Legends laundromat had seen quite a lot over the years.

'Did you hear about Bob Hawke?' Therese asked the old lady.

'Well, I don't know. We were just talking about it. Poor old Bob. We'll see if this young fellow can do anything. But, you know, the bus driver fellow, he said that we'll all forget about them. About Bob Hawke. We'll all be forgotten. And I don't know. That's not want you want to hear when you're my age.'

'Oh you won't be forgot, Nan. Don't you think, mate?' And Therese looked at me.

I looked at them, the nice old lady with the barking dog philosophy of life, the huge blackclad transexual and all those movie stars making love to the camera there in the laundromat.

'No,' I said slowly, 'I will not forget you.'

I walked home, switched the television on and watched Paul Keating sit awkwardly behind a desk in the new Parliament House and give his first press conference as prime minister.

He wasn't as free and easy as he had been after his first tilt at Hawke, where he was defeated. Then he was all off-the-cuff charisma, full of sporting analogies. 'I had one shot to fire in the locker room and it wasn't enough. I wanted his job and he didn't want to give it to me. Simple as that.'

He had smiled and looked almost handsome. Well, he'd looked relaxed.

But this time it was as if the words stuck in his mouth a bit. As if he was conscious of it being important and he wanted to make sure he sounded statesmanlike.

Maybe he was just a little nervous.

He spoke about what it meant to him to lead the Labor Party and what it meant to lead Australia, to be a prime minister for all Australians.

I looked at Paul Keating and thought of the Australians I had come across that night. The bus driver, the old lady, her neighbour, the guys in the car park of the brothel and the two junkies on the 216. 'Go Bombers.'

I looked at the television and thought of them. 'Well good luck, mate.'

The next day I rang my mother.

'What does Dad think about Keating?' I asked.

'Oh not much, he doesn't really think about anything much these days. Although he always liked Keating.'

'Did he?'

'I think so. Anyway. It's not really like his party anymore. It's more out of habit than thought. You've got to back somebody.'

I didn't know what to say so I filled a silence with the story of the old lady and the dog.

'Well why didn't the silly cow go and do something?'

'Well, I don't know. Maybe she thought she couldn't. She seemed like a nice old lady.'

'Good God. What is the point of the story?'

I didn't know. But something about it struck me as memorable.

There was a groan at the end of the telephone line. I offered to talk to one of the dogs.

'Why would they waste their breath on you? Anyway they're tied up across the street barking.'

'Oh come on, Mum.'

'Come on yourself. Sometimes it's hard to do the right thing. Sometimes you can't do the right thing. But Jesus, the least you can do is admit that you've no stomach for it. She wouldn't be the first person to put up with the noise, let it become part of your life, rather than do something about it.'

•

If Bob Hawke had been everyone's idea of a suburban jock and had never looked out of place at any sporting event then Keating walked the other side of the street. Hawke may have been the star of his own melodramatic soapie but he was a type recognised by almost every Australian: a lad writ large.

Keating was something else. He was full of a blokey vocabulary, which became even more pronounced as his political career wore on. He used words as weapons, odd bits of vernacular like hand grenades, to mock and ridicule. 'You are just a shiver looking for a spine to run up,' he growled at Peter Reith.

The Liberal leader John Hewson was busy waving the keys to his Ferrari with the cry that, 'I hope every Australian can one day own and drive a Ferrari.' He was like a general waving a sabre to his army, exalting Australians to achieve and to strive. He and his political manifesto, 'Fightback', seemed unbeatable, especially compared to the ragged visage of Bob Hawke.

The great irony of Keating is that he used the ultimate weapon of the Australian sporting boofhead to undermine Hewson. Sledging.

The parliamentary highlights package on the news became akin to a sports report. Keating mocking and bullying Hewson and his frontbench.

'Why won't you call an early election?' bellowed Hewson to Keating.

'Because, mate, I want to do you slowly.' Keating smiled and added a sporting wink.

Matters of state were at stake, and they were debated, but the wider public was eating up the show. It was personality politics, theatrics in Question Time, and Keating played his part in full.

In the first few months of taking office some of Keating's performances could almost have been ripped from 'Coach Talk', a form of histrionic hyperbole that sporting coaches use to gee up their teams.

I can remember lying in bed one night and listening to a snippet of Keating's 'Tug the Forelock' speech about how the opposition parties were 'the lickspittles of their betters in England and how afraid the conservative parties were of being Australian'.

As I lay there I felt like pulling up my football socks, sucking in my breath and chewing down on my mouthguard. Bursting to get out and tackle the first opposition player I saw. Getting Reith just under the ribs or maybe mining away at the bottom of the ruck I'd find Hewson himself and go to work with my elbows. Only it wasn't a game of Rugby. And Keating wasn't my coach. But somehow, if you were up for it, the lines were getting crossed between national debate and national pastimes.

Keating didn't need to hang out at grand finals, test matches or the Melbourne Cup to make a link between politics and sport, he was turning it into one. If he went to a sporting event he looked as out of place as a man could be. 'That bastard is sitting there humming Mahler or Mendelssohn or whatever it is he listens to, he's not watching the footy,' said a friend.

On some nights he was the best show in town.

I was sitting in the kitchen of a systems analyst who'd recently been retrenched. I had a part in a movie set in an estate – it was supposed to be a horror film but it wasn't as scary as the place we were filming in.

I was made up with a crazed hairdo and bursting brain, and he had a chenille bathrobe on and lots of gold jewellery.

We were filming in his backyard and he was worried that the crew might damage the wood-panelled spa he had recently installed.

It looked like the panelling on Mrs Glazier's television and the water looked just as green as the images on that telly.

'Oh we had a bit of fun the other night with a little bit of food colouring,' explained the systems analyst. 'You take sugar, mate?'

I nodded my head with its exploding brain.

'Yes, pretty good set-up. But you know it's always easy to shit in your nest when things look good.'

Me and my brain looked up at the systems analyst.

'How's that mate?' I said.

'Well we like to think of fun things to do out here of a weekend. And, you know, there's the odd party or two. But one thing leads to another. And a Rocky Horror theme party one weekend can lead to something like wife swapping and a bit of food colouring in your spa. Here's your coffee.'

My brain and I said thanks.

'I was a little worried and I rang up the fellow at the pool place in the plaza but he didn't seem to think there would be too much of a problem. Then the missus cracked the shits a bit. Took off for a while. Dare say she'll be back, but it does get a little lonely.'

The coffee had at least half of Bundaberg's annual sugar crop in it and I gagged a bit so I couldn't ask whether the missus had cracked the shits over the wife swapping or the green food dye, or whether the two were mixed up in the whole business.

The systems analyst didn't elaborate but chatted away in a rather distant manner.

'It's easy to shit in your nest, look at Keating and Hewson. Look how the telly and the papers treat them.'

The systems analyst went on to explain his theory. The press and the rest of us had fallen into the personality game and although we had forgotten about Fightback, the proposed GST and a whole rack of other bits and pieces of national debate, it had basically come down to a slugfest between the arts-loving bovver boy Keating and Hewson, the close-eyed merchant banker with a funny haircut who couldn't say his 'r's and drove around in a fancy sports car.

'Hewson is a mad missionary and Keating is a mad Catholic and they both pretend to know what we go through. Politicians aren't normal like you and me. What sort of normal bloke goes knocking on doors to beg for your vote, to pretend to care?' The systems analyst laughed without smiling.

He stood in his bathrobe and bling maintaining a vigil over his fake wood-panelled, wife-swapping spa filled with food colouring and I sat with my exploding brain and we drank coffee. And we were normal. I wished some politician would come knocking. But sadly we had to entertain ourselves.

'I should hate this bloody government. The interest is killing on this place, I get on top of the payments and then I get retrenched. I get a package, I get the house, the spa.'

'The parties,' I added.

He nodded.

'Yeah, I get the parties…but really. I still watch the telly at night to see what Keating's going to do to that Hewson. He Road Runnered him you know. Meep Meep. In the bloody parliament.' He didn't laugh this time. 'It's like the fucking football. It's all just a show. It used to mean something.'

It's all just a show. Did he mean that it was all pretending? Or that sport and politics were close to becoming entertainment. Sports, or what we thought of as the marquee sports, the important sports, were increasingly becoming a part of the entertainment business.

Cricket, football and tennis were important sports because you could make money from them. And that was why you saw so much of them.

I doubted whether you could ever fill the MCG for Question Time. But the televising of parliamentary proceedings had added a layer of showtime to national affairs.

Keating, it was said, had been against the televising of parliament. While he seemingly had an advantage in the nightly berating of his opponents it could well be he sensed a double-edged sword. It was hard to turn away from gangster talk quite so evenly. The difference between the two Keatings – the arts admirer and the sledger – were vast.

It certainly seemed that way to Aunty Rita. Although the only time she'd ever voted Labor was to cast a ballot for my father, and that was just the once.

'Let me tell you, your fellow Keating's not right. He's like something out of an Anthony Hopkins movie. Eating people by day and polishing his French clocks and humming Mahler or whatever it is he listens to by night.'

Keating's enthusiam for the arts was as strong as Hawke's love of sports, but nobody ever questioned Bob Hawke's sanity.

I was in the Legends Laundromat one night drying my clothes. Therese was there and a man who walked outside to spit occasionally. The old lady from the 216 wasn't anywhere to be seen.

It was late and Therese had a bit of a growth happening. She yawned with a great stretch and scratched the prickles on her cheeks.

'Man, I'm tired,' she said to nobody in particular.

'Been working hard?' I asked

She shrugged and nodded. 'That and the bloody Olympics. I've fallen in love with Barcelona. Those divers. The landscape.' She shook her big hands in delight. 'It just seems so sensual. Those bodies in the air and the city behind, I have never seen such athletic bodies. And the French woman in the white one-piece. Oh. Twirling in the air like an angel with that church behind her.'

She laughed and shook her head.

'We're doing well,' I said.

'Yes we are. Kieren did well, didn't he?' Kieren Perkins had won the 1500 metres.

'You remember Steve Holland?' I asked.

She shook her head.

'It's just great to see them get a bit of support and see them do well. It's not cheap but it makes you feel good. Money well spent. And it's more artistic than just normal sport too, you know.'

The opening ceremony in particular had taken Therese's fancy. An archer had shot a flaming arrow through the sky to light the Olympic flame.

'Now that was a fantastic show, like a ballet. And you know that fella was handicapped, only had a couple of fingers on one hand. Read in the paper.'

The man smiled and mimed shooting the arrow.

Therese turned to him. 'You see! How good was it, mate?' She laughed. 'And you know all the money they give out to stuff you never see, all those weird people who get that fifty grand from Keating to weave baskets or make up shitty poetry, that fella without his fingers means more. Kieren Perkins means more. Suppose it's just horses for courses.'

I looked at her and thought that Kieren probably cost ten times as much as the recipients of the Creative Nation initiatives.

But then Kieren was from a glamour sport. I don't think badminton or table tennis or archery would have been bankrolled, they belonged to the sausage sizzle and lucky raffle sports.

There were never that many Creative Nation fellowships given out but newspapers always unearthed some undeserving basket weaver or pianist who had received a grant. So the whole scheme was an outrageous waste of money according to Therese and the newspaper she read.

I could have said that sending a team of three hundred athletes to the other side of the world when the majority had little chance of success was a waste of money.

I could have said that if you wanted efficiency and value for your dollar only a smaller number should have gone.

I didn't say anything, of course.

'It's not like Keating's educated, not like he went to uni. I got more education than him. It's all for show, him and the arty fartys. He doesn't like sport so, you know, he's got to celebrate the arty mob cause he's so smart – he's just another fucking bloke in a suit.' She didn't say it with any great passion, just in a manner that assumed I would agree with her and the paper she read.

The man spat outside and Therese went home to watch her divers in the skies above Barcelona.

Not long after that I thought of Therese's neighbour, the old lady from the 216. I thought of her barking dog. If there's a problem and it's worrying you, change your thinking on it. Ignore it, live with it, change your thinking on it.

The uncomfortable thing about Keating for Australians was that he challenged their ability to ignore the world. He made people take a look.

It wasn't good enough to change your thinking anymore.

He didn't float above people like Gough Whitlam did, and he didn't embrace them to be king of the kids like Bob Hawke. The best of Keating was when he stood in his nice suits with all of his idiosyncratic manner and gave it to the country with both barrels.

December 1992 was such a time. He stood in Redfern and in his unadorned formal speaking voice, which to me always seemed a little bland and uncertain, made a series of statements about what had happened to the Indigenous peoples of Australia since European settlement.

My mother rang me up the night it was broadcast on the news.

'Did you hear that speech?' she said after I had said hello to her dog.

'Keating's?'

'Yes. He's a funny one. It's the sort of speech your father was waiting for. All that shouting the lad does and pretending to be tough. A wind would probably knock him over, you know. But he's opened a door with that one.'

My father had died a year before.

I said the speech had seemed good.

There was a pause and then my mother spoke quite firmly. 'It's the sort of thing that plants a seed. Moments don't come along too often and when they do it's important to know they happened. You are a stupid boy sometimes.'

Some time later I walked around the Melbourne Agricultural Show and through the government pavilion. Little hands grabbed free pencils, Chinese horoscopes and bits and pieces of give-away information. Names were called out by ragged parents in an attempt to control excited kids. Kids with painted faces were told not to fight over showbags and to be nice and share, words that were no doubt told to the parents who uttered them years before when they were kids. The noise was familiar and fun, and intense.

One exhibit began playing an audio tape of Keating's Redfern speech. As the speech went on in his oddly lifeless voice, more and more people began to listen. Children were told to shush and pay attention. By the end there seemed to be hundreds of people simply standing and listening and, as the last words were spoken, applause rang out from those there.

But, of course, some people listening in a hall isn't really indicative of what goes on outside that hall. You tend to gravitate to what you want to hear, but I think there were a few there who experienced the power that emotive words uttered with meaning can produce. And, of course, there were some who didn't.

I looked around and, just past an applauding couple, were hundreds more people going about their business, not really listening but simply looking and poking at other stalls. Keating's words were just more noise, a background to shop to.

A man behind clapped his hands and his daughter asked him why he was doing it. 'I'm not quite sure, darling, but it's polite to say thank you to the people putting on the show.' He indicated some face-painting clowns who were twisting balloons into animal shapes.

When I found myself joining in, I thought of an old dog barking and barking and barking. But maybe I had it wrong. Maybe they were applauding the balloon animals.

But then anybody can be a sucker for getting caught up in an event.

I was driving in Melbourne one late afternoon in a temperamental XP Falcon during peak hour, on my way to a meeting.

A meeting I had guaranteed to keep. I had promised the person down the other end of the phone line that I would be there.

'I've told you I'm a busy person. Don't be late,' said the voice.

She paused and I took this as an indication I was supposed to speak.

'Well, I know and I'm sorry but I will be there.'

'Yes.' She hung up.

She was the most uncivil civil celebrant that I had ever come across.

I had picked her out of the Yellow Pages to perform the official duties at my wedding. I was organising the wedding.

Or rather I was reorganising. The first time it had fallen through when my father became ill.

And as this woman's number was the only civil celebrant I had I just rang her again. I don't know why really, she was even ruder than she was the first time.

I had suggested an outdoor service.

'Oh an outdoors service. You're not one of those people?'

'One of what people?'

'One of those people who can't afford a nice hall or restaurant for the ceremony.'

I told her that we were planning to use the local Kentucky Fried Chicken restaurant but it was booked for a Young Liberals meeting.

'You're trying to be funny, aren't you? I don't find my work amusing.'

I should have said thanks but no thanks. But I made an appointment and I guaranteed to keep it, on Australia Day 1993.

I drove in a relatively good mood. The traffic was a bit heavier than I thought it would be, a hangover perhaps from the Australia Day parade that had taken place in the city earlier. It was a special Australia Day for a number of reasons.

First, it was the last time that the national day was to be a long weekend. After 1993 the day it fell on was to be the public holiday. One of my neighbours, an old man who spent most of his time underneath the bonnet of his car after a lifetime of working and serving in World War II and Korea – 'I always fancied me desserts' was his reply when I asked why he'd served in two conflicts – wasn't impressed.

'Trust a bloody Tory to go and ruin a long weekend. All so some silly buggers can go wave a flag.'

Well, that was the future.

On that particular Australia Day the parade, complete with bagpipes, military bands, and bussed-in school children to fill out the sparse crowds of uninterested shoppers and workers, meandered through the city streets.

I'd always liked parades. I told this to my mother who informed me that that was only because a parade meant nothing else was going on. It was a holiday.

It was the last time that the Australia Day was to work around the people and their lives, the last time that Australia Day just sort of happened. The last time before it became an event.

The parade went off as well as you could hope, the Victorian premier Jeff Kennett was heckled during his speech by somebody who kept shouting out for more public transport until the twenty-one gun salute went off. Then the heckler advised Kennett to, 'Duck your head, Jeff.'

Kennett just smiled and laughed a little.

Kurdish women had protested on the steps of Parliament House but they had been moved on to make way for the premier and other dignitaries. After they were gone nobody seemed to have any idea why they were protesting.

But none of this explained the traffic.

I looked at my watch, there was enough time to make it to the uncivil celebrant, even though the wheels rolled slowly.

And there was always the cricket. That was the other thing about this Australia Day. The West Indies and Australia were playing in Adelaide. If Australia won the test they won the series. An unthinkable event, for the routine plundering of Australia by the men from the Caribbean was an almost biennial event in the summer months.

But this time Australia was one up in the series and a wobbly old off spinner with a bad knee called Tim May had cleaned up the Windies on a turning pitch. Australia was a day's batting away from winning the Frank Worrell Trophy. They needed only 186 runs.

A day away but it might as well have been a universe. The West Indian quicks had got stuck into the top order and all the name players of the Australian team had fallen by the wayside. Only a stocky little number three from Western Australia called Justin Langer, making his debut with his tapping left-handed stance, had put up any show. After nearly having his head knocked into next week with a ball from Ambrose that my father would have called a Scone Bunter, Langer tapped away and tapped and tapped.

But then as the traffic slowed and the parade had passed and Australia Day had sort of happened, the real event began.

Turning on the radio, trapped in the car, I listened with an increasing amount of panic and hope. Not being able to see what was happening made it even worse in that almost unbearable, exciting way.

Any inflection in the commentators' voices, any exclamation, any sigh or rise and fall in the roar of the crowd would cause heart rates to jump and provoke cries of anguish.

You could see that by the traffic jam.

One old man in a Jaguar up ahead seemed to have forgotten his left indicator was on. After awhile he turned it off and, almost immediately, Shane Warne, who'd been weaving his way around the bouncers from the West Indian bowlers for over an hour, was trapped on the crease by a ball from Ian Bishop. There was an appeal and an awful wait. The Jag in front lurched, both brake lights went on and you could see by the way he was snatching that the old man was trying to flick his indicator back on.

He wasn't quick enough because Warne was out.

The old man in front held his hands to his head like a demented scientist and then kept his indicator flashing. He kept driving with his indicator on, but nobody beeped their horn at him because we all understood he was simply following the old superstition of doing something to keep the good luck going your team's way.

Up in the team's dressing room at the Adelaide Oval the Australian captain Allan Border sat flipping a cricket ball from one hand to another. The old man had the indicator. A man in a red Commodore slowly circled a roundabout again and again and again. As he drove around you could hear him saying, 'Come on, come on, come on!' Another day he might have been lost, but on that Australia Day one look would have told you that he was listening to the cricket.

After a while the last man in, McDermott, the red-headed pace bowler from Ipswich in Queensland, started to look solid enough. The indicator was doing its trick. Tim May, the wobbly off spinner with the bad knee, started scoring runs.

Neville Oliver the tweedy sounding ABC commentator started daring to suggest that a close finish was 'in the offing'. Whatever that clichéd sports commentator's chestnut actually meant, everybody in a block of cars understood what was being promised.

I can't remember who started it first, but at the end of each over when no Australian wicket had fallen somebody beeped their horn. Then another car joined at the end of another over until a chorus of horns sounded in one short little blast.

I looked around and could see people in their cars helping Australia along. Two women laughed out loud. A podgy man with wraparound sunglasses, which looked like they'd been pinched from his teenage son, beeped his horn with an almost imperceptible tilt of his head. After each over he would beep and then tilt his head a little.

I looked at my watch and realised that I wasn't going to make my appointment with the uncivil civil celebrant. I had to call her, but if I called her then I wouldn't be there to beep. I would break the pattern.

My car was stuck in the traffic close to a public telephone box, which were relatively plentiful back then. I could wait for the drinks break – Neville Oliver said it was only an over away. I swore to myself. And I swore about the uncivil civil celebrant; she had almost made me miss a beep. Even the tilting head man seemed to surreptitiously look at me with a warning not to let the team down.

Red-headed McDermott and wobbily kneed May made it through to the drinks break.

I opened the door of the car, put the gear to neutral, handbraked and ran to the phone box. Then I had to run back. The phone money, lots of loose change, was in the ashtray of the old Falcon. The ashtray was little. I have big hands. I yelled. Finally I got some money and ran to the phone. I still had more time. The news headlines were on and I could hear them, not only from my window but from all the other cars.

Some suitably deep, sensible middle-aged voice moaned on about how John Hewson and Peter Reith had got stuck into

Paul Keating's piggery investments and then Paul Keating really got stuck into John Hewson about him minimising his tax in the 1980s.

I pushed the coins into the phone's slot. More than I needed. The uncivil civil celebrant was only about a block and a half away. I was breathing hard.

Now the sensible voice spoke about the Australia Day Honours. Mandawuy Yunupingu was Australian of the Year and Kieren Perkins, fresh from Barcelona and all those beautiful divers, was Young Australian of the Year.

The phone rang. And rang. And rang.

Soon the news headlines would go to the weather and then... I muttered under my breath.

'Hellooooooooo,' said the voice down the other end of the line.

'It's me.'

'Pardon?'

'It's me!' I shrieked again.

Silence

'I can't make it. I can't make it.'

'Who is this please?' she said in a fruity voice. A mad image flashed through my head of Danny La Rue.

'It's me, William McInnes, I am sorry but I can't make it this afternoon. I —'

She cut me off with a sound that was a mixture between someone clearing their throat and an angry Viking blowing into some big horn.

'Well. I have told you Mr... what's your name?'

The sensible voice had gone onto the weather. I was going to miss the first ball back.

'Look it's William McInnes, I was the guy who was going to get married outdoors.'

'Oh – the Kentucky Fried Chicken man!' said the uncivil civil celebrant.

The sensible voice said, 'And now it's back to Neville Oliver at the Adelaide Oval.'

'Look,' I almost screamed, 'I have to go. I'm sorry. I have to beep, I have to beep. For May and McDermott!'

'What?'

I ran back to the car, clipped on my seatbelt, put the car into gear and got ready to toot.

I had made it. I looked back to the phone. It was off the hook.

I like to think that she could have heard all those radios down the line as she Vikinged away. I'd left some coins on the shelf. I didn't care.

The Jag still indicated, the podgy man was ready to tilt. I had done my bit.

Neville Oliver's voice sounded like it belonged to someone who loved a packet a day. There was a tobacco quality about it. I felt like smoking. The longer he talked, the more I felt like one.

The indicator twitched, the horns beeped – we were still in it.

For another forty minutes we tooted at the end of the over. Only three runs to win. May fended a ball off his hip and they ran for one. Neville Oliver gurgled that there was a chance for a run-out, they were thinking of a second run which would have tied it. I held my breath, there were a few odd shrieks from some cars.

'No,' came the tobacco tones of Oliver. 'No, they didn't take the second, McDermott sent May back.'

'Oh there was a run there,' said the expert commentator, who I think was Terry Jenner.

'Why didn't you run?' I said to the steering wheel.

One run to win.

Then McDermott got a short ball from Courtney Walsh. He tried to turn his body away. He tried not to duck. Whether he hit the ball was immaterial. I knew as soon as I heard the catch in Neville Oliver's throat. Like he wanted to slag a huge golly.

Red-headed McDermott was out. He trudged off with brave, wobbly kneed May.

Allan Border hurled the cricket ball he'd been gently tossing into the wall of the dressing-room.

I emitted a yelp and a long, low moan on the horn.

Australia was beaten. The traffic dispersed quite quickly. The Jag's indicator went off sadly and the podgy guy took off the silly sunglasses and looked over to me.

He smiled and shrugged his shoulders.

I couldn't help but feel a little responsible. Bloody uncivil civil celebrant.

I drove out along the eastern freeway to where I was having dinner with my wife-to-be, if we could ever find somebody to marry us, and her family.

I sat in the car for a little while. I had shared something so madly communal and yet had not uttered a single word to any other person save the marriage celebrant.

I had to go in and tell my wife-to-be that my celebrant had fallen through and was, for all intents and purposes, still frothing down the phone line.

I walked into the house and there was the woman I loved and all her family. They turned to me with flushed faces.

'Why didn't they run?' yelled my wife-to-be.

'Did you see it?' she said to me.

'Hear it? Did you hear it?' said her father

I looked at them

'The CRICKET!' yelled my wife-to-be. 'How good was that!'

'Why didn't they run on that ball!' said her father. 'That's a Queenslander for you.'

I looked at them and laughed. It didn't matter about uncivil celebrants. I was now completely undone. She had me at 'Why didn't they run.'

We'd all shared it. They had all sat in the same seats while watching the game on television.

Her dad couldn't decide whether to listen to the commentary from the television or turn it down and listen to the ABC radio.

'We had to find something that worked.'

Sport in its purest sense is something you share and enjoy – even when the team that you barrack for gets done. Even with all the will in the world, sometimes they just can't get over the line. And even though you get that disappointment, that shard of failure, you can't help but feel that something wonderful has been shared.

And part of that appeal of sport was beginning to be diminished.

My wife-to-be's family and their footy allegiances were a prime example of what happens when rationalisation takes over a game, when a sport becomes a business.

When they arrived in Melbourne from the Snowy Hydro town of Cooma all the members of the family had to go through the same preliminary ritual of the great southern capital.

When the father and his three daughters went to work and school the first thing asked of them was, 'Who do you go for?' What team did they barrack for? It's easier if you are just born into a team, but to choose your allegiance is a tricky business, especially when you fly blind with the field from which to choose.

The safest best was to ask the person who asked you, 'Who do you go for?' Who should I go for?

So it was when they returned home that all four found that they all supported different clubs.

The father went for Carlton because a fellow engineer was a Carlton supporter.

The eldest daughter became an Essendon supporter, the middle one went for Hawthorn and the youngest a Richmond supporter.

When the economics began to bite in the early 1990s it was no longer who a fellow at work barracked for, or what the team of the kid down the street was, the choice of teams came down to brand power and the marketing appeal of clubs became a dominant force.

I found myself going for the Footscray Bulldogs because I could wander down to their home ground at three-quarter time, enter for nothing and watch the play at the messy Western Oval, which was chock-full of character as well as the wild westerly winds that blew from the Geelong Road end.

I fell for the crowd as much as the players. The half-time entertainment was unlike anything I had ever seen, or was ever likely to see. At the major break, the Hyde Street Yarraville

Band would play the theme songs of the Doggies and their opponents. The band would make their way around the oval and the real highlight was what followed.

Four men carried a blanket and people tossed in money for the band.

The first time I saw this, the band marched and the blanket-carriers ambled along behind. Three blanket-carriers had head protection: a hard hat, a cricket helmet and a full-face bike helmet. The carrier at the front, who was bareheaded, looked around to see what his colleagues were wearing. He began to fidget and twitch like a bad actor in an old war movie where troops were about to go over the top.

I was thinking, to use one of my mum's expressions, that he wasn't quite right, when something happened that explained his tics.

From nowhere an avalanche of coins hailed down upon the blanket and the blanket-carriers.

The three helmeted men gamely staggered on while the hatless lead carrier danced and ducked and flinched like a character from a Sam Peckinpah movie, although instead of a hail of gunfire it was twenty cent, ten cent, and the dreaded fifty cent pieces.

A man next to me roared with laughter. 'Got 'im! Got 'im on the melon with a fifty-center!'

I thought the bareheaded blanket-carrier was grimacing but then I recognised he was laughing, and he was still laughing at the beginning of the third quarter.

He came smiling up to the bar at the Barkly Street end and ordered a beer.

He was slapped on the back.

'Good for you, Deadly!' said a man who looked like he had just carried down the ten commandments from the mountain.

Another reason to follow the Doggies, they were Moses' chosen team.

Deadly turned and gave him a thumbs up. Little bumps dotted his forehead.

'How much you get?' asked Moses.

'Hundred dollars,' sniffed Deadly.

'Good man,' said Moses.

It was explained to me that Deadly, whoever he was, had taken a bet to walk around with the blanket with no head gear. The money went to the band.

'Are you in the band, mate?' I asked as he passed by me.

'No, mate, can't play. Only tune I blow is out me arse. Just helping out.'

And he went and sipped his Vic Bitter and rubbed his head.

How can you economically rationalise that sort of club entertainment? That sort of sport?

Well, it was beginning, and by the decade's end no games would be played at the Western Oval and it no longer mattered who was coming home in the fourth quarter with the mighty wind from Geelong Road behind their backs.

Lots of people, people like my wife, started to drift away from sport, simply because they didn't like it being shoved at them as an all-important event every day of the week.

But then lots of people seemed to like it too. That was the way of the world. Keating boasted that he had opened up the country to the world. Blowing away the cobwebs, making the economy and business more streamlined and user-friendly. That's what happened to the Hyde Street band, blown away like cobwebs, for there was no place for brass bands in modern mass entertainment.

Keating certainly had a lot on his hands because in early 1993 John Hewson crisscrossed the country during the federal election and held 'old-style election town hall' meetings. This meant that he screamed himself hoarse in front of his supporters chanting, 'Keating's got to go, Keating's got to go!' Keating, on the other hand, was banging on incessantly about the GST and the 'feral abacus' that was the good Dr John.

The whole feel of the election campaign was more like a sporting event. Supporters from both sides seemed to get their jollies chanting choruses like a school sporting house at a swimming carnival.

It was Keating versus Dr John. The fact that Hewson wouldn't talk to any 'serious' members of the press and instead stayed committed to losing his voice in car parks, halls and where-have-you lowered the standards of debate to an even greater simplicity. It was a scare campaign. As election night drew near there was a feeling that my side, my team, the Labor Party, was going to get hammered. It had reached that level.

My wife stayed at home heavily pregnant and told me to go out and have a couple for both of us because it might be the last time we would have a Labor government for a while. I went to the inner-city warehouse loft of a friend and there seven of us slumped around the television to watch the carnage.

What unfurled that night was just an election, but what also happened was that election night became an event. The seats from Tasmania came through, and all of them went to Labor. I got a phone call from my wife who said that she was halfway through a tub of cappuccino swirl ice-cream and was working out calculations of what the swing would mean if it was across the board for Labor.

She told me to have a few drinks for both of us because it might be a good night after all.

When it became clear that the Labor Party had won, it was as close to winning a grand final that I have ever come. Hysteria was everywhere. The election had been reduced to so simple and basic a level that it had become a game.

Hewson emerged at the Wentworth Hotel looking stunned, his eyes even closer together than ever, he went beyond looking cross-eyed. He was on auto-pilot but somehow he and his stunned-looking family gathered like strangers by a podium and managed to get through his concession speech. If you could call what he attempted to give a concession speech.

'Jesus, he's a fucking train wreck,' said a friend.

Hewson obviously only had one speech to give and tried to tailor it to a defeat. He numbly spoke about daring to dream. I thought of Uncle Royce and his take on dreams and how they can turn out to be funny things to try to hold onto.

After the election, before the start of the new term, Keating apparently called Hewson over for a brief chat behind the Speaker's chair. He asked Hewson how he felt, for he thought he must feel terrible. Keating told Hewson that the things he had said about him, he didn't really mean. That he had respect for Hewson. It was all part of the show.

What happens on the field stays on the field.

But that was after the election. That night we all just stared at the train wreck that was one man's political dream.

It was ghastly until someone slowly said, 'What do you think Keating is doing now?'

We all burst out laughing. People were screaming and cheering at the television. Yelling like it was the football. We screamed at Hewson. We screamed at the journalists on the panels like my father used to yell at football commentators. Our team did well. When Keating came and made his famous speech at the Bankstown Sports Club against the regal deep blue of the draped curtains it was just him with a cameo from his wife, Annita.

The crowd chanted, 'We want Paul.'

He smiled and said, 'You've got me!'

He called it the sweetest victory of all. One for the true believers. He said it would be a long time before an Australian political party tried to place one group of Australians in one area and another group in another area. A long time before Australians would be divided.

We kicked on for a little while longer and then I stumbled out and bought a *Herald Sun* that had proclaimed a victory to Hewson in its banner headline. I walked through the streets of Melbourne and the longer I walked it seemed that those streets belonged to another Saturday night. Nothing special. I began to think that maybe not everyone's team had won. That not everyone cared. Up by Elizabeth Street a guy dressed up for a night on the town weaved his way towards King Street and the strip of clubs that loitered in that part of the city. He broke off from his group of mates and he finally staggered to halt in the middle of the tram tracks and assumed the position. He stood there urinating. 'Go Bombers!' he bellowed.

I caught the 216 and sat bouncing gently along Dynon Road. The purple light came on just by the Doris and Rock Tender Touch.

Nobody spoke. A moth clung and then flung itself against the ultraviolet light. Even against the sound of the engine and the compressed gears you could hear it hitting the light casing. Again and again and again.

I tried to close my eyes and think of something else. Keating.

He was right, it had been a victory for the true believers. Maybe he knew, though, standing there with his name being chanted that there simply weren't enough of those true believers to really make it matter. Maybe he knew that most people had voted for the fear campaign against the GST.

He was a smart man. He had buried enough political bodies and hopes and dreams to know how mortal political careers could be. But in that moment of victory I wonder if he even let a part of his mind think of what the future may have in wait.

It wouldn't be that long before an Australian political party divided the population and rode the waves of division to power. Divided them with the majority's consent and agreement. And by the decade's end a GST would be in place.

The moth hit the canopy again and again. My team had won. The talking heads on the election panel had called it history, but maybe it had just been another chapter in the game. Keating had opened many doors, but the trick is to have people walk through. Lots of things seemed possible that night. A republic. Reconciliation. But I heard a noise. Like a dog barking in the night. A desperate barking that wouldn't go away. I opened my eyes and I saw that apart from the silent driver, and that moth, I sat alone in the purple light.

# 8

Perhaps it was because the hammer fell on my head. Or perhaps I am making more out of it than I should, but I hold Mr Darcy responsible for the last few years of the twentieth century.

Or perhaps it was because the hammer fell on my head. That was why I unleashed a maelstrom of bonnets and lace, and low brows and bad accents. The bloody hammer.

I was visiting my mother for the weekend and I foolishly asked if there was anything she'd like done. I love that expression. Would you 'like anything done?'

'Well, I've my new set of teeth so you can't help there.' And she took a few moments to come up with something. She'd recently, in her words, had an incident with her bottom plate but she had organised a new set and all was well in her world, or so I thought.

'Well,' she said, almost licking her lips, 'you could take me to see the new *Pride and Prejudice* or you might like to fix the gate.'

And she smiled.

I shuddered. There was no way I was going to see *Pride and Prejudice*, whether it was new or not. So, gritting my teeth, I tried to be jolly, 'Right then, the gate it is.'

It was a forlorn hope. I knew as much about gate fixing as the pope does about panelbeating. I may be selling the Holy Father short, but there you are.

The gate wouldn't shut properly and I set about fixing it up. My mother handily supplied the tools: a thirty-year-old sander that gave you an electric shock when you turned it on, a hammer that I think once belonged to Thor the Thunder God, and some oily bits and pieces that sat in the bottom of an old jam jar.

I sanded and swore and banged and had some serious words with the sander and accidentally stood on the dog. That is when the hammer fell. On my head.

I gave up on the gate after nearly shaving my arm to the bone with the sander and proclaimed to my mother that I was ready to take her to the movies to see the new *Pride and Prejudice*. I must have been suffering from concussion.

We wandered off to a shopping centre that had been built, as local legend had it, on a bora ring – a place where Indigenous Australians would meet for ceremonies and dance.

'Why don't they put a plaque up here to commemorate it?' I asked. 'They've got all those other places marked.'

'Oh that'd be right,' said my mother. 'Nobody knows for certain it was here. Never any concrete mention of it, it might put some people off shopping here.' She paused for a moment and came up with another idea, 'More like people just couldn't give a fig about it. Shame.'

We settled into a cinema named after a family who had owned a toy shop and a sawmill on the peninsula. And a big yacht. All these things had passed and now all that was left was the name of the cinema. That was more than the bora ring.

'Old Mr Thurecht was quite nice, you know,' Mum said as she settled into the comfy seats.

I remembered buying old model aircraft from the Thurecht toy shop, but I couldn't remember Old Mr Thurecht.

I told this to my mother.

'Yes, well, that's not surprising.'

We chatted about the film we were about to watch as my mother went through the sweets she had bought – a mixed bag.

'All the nice odds and sods.' She smiled.

Why the world needed a new *Pride and Prejudice* is open to debate, but I guess they keep on making Commodores so why can't they keep on making *Pride and Prejudice*s?

'Maybe they should make a car and call it *Pride and Prejudice*,' I said.

'Are you trying to be funny?' my mother said. 'Because if you are I don't want to sit with you.'

I promised I'd behave.

'Good boy. Would you like a lolly?'

And so we sat and watched the new *Pride and Prejudice*. As it started my mother whispered, 'Would you like to have some teeth? Do you remember Dad and the teeth?'

I laughed. I used to like eating lolly teeth. My father would bring bags of lollies back from the RSL on a Sunday night and we'd all put the lolly teeth in and pretend to be Liberace.

Dad would sit at the table and put the big lolly teeth in and try and talk with an American accent.

I laughed thinking about him. A big, flushed working man back from a night at the Returned Servicemen's League, back from a night with his mates. He'd whistle and sing his way home along the beach and always make sure that he'd come back with bags of lollies for us from the corner shop on Sydney Street.

'Well he's earned the right to a drink or two,' my mum would say. 'They all went and fought the country so let them have their time.'

I was fine with that, especially if it meant lollies.

In the cinema, I laughed. 'Yes, thanks,' I said and took a lolly. Even as I held them briefly in my hand before popping them in my gob, something in my hammer-concussed brain sent a little warning signal that they were a lot harder than I remembered.

I started to suck on them and realised as soon as I felt my mother shaking in laughter next to me that they weren't the lolly teeth I remembered.

'Oh Jesus! Mum! *Mum!* Oh Christ!'

I spat the broken dentures into my hand.

'Oh, Mum,' I said sadly, looking at her in the dark.

She was wiping tears away from her eyes. 'Knew they'd come in handy.'

Behind us a voice I half recognised as belonging to an old man who used to run a bakery sang out, 'Steady, young Bill, the movie can't be that bad, it's only just started!'

'Choked on a lolly,' guffawed my mother. 'Got to be careful the way memories can creep up on you. Things can be different from what you remember!' She laughed on and off for the rest of the movie, which was a considerable achievement for we sat and we sat and we sat.

It was okay as far as *Pride and Prejudice*s go, I guess. Keira Knightley did some odd things with her jaw on occasions. Maybe she'd fallen for the old broken denture trick. The old man behind us, who used to make the most beautiful pies in his bakery, offered that Keira, 'Looks like a bloody piranha, the way she goes on with her gob.'

But my mum couldn't care less about Keira, or Lizzy as she was called in the new *Pride and Prejudice*. She was interested in Mr Darcy.

Mr Darcy. I rubbed my head.

'What do you think,' she asked, 'about Mr Darcy?'

'What is it about Mr Darcy and women?'

'Mr Darcy? What is it about him? It's happy endings, you stupid boy. It's the unattainable romance of it all. We've all got our Mr Darcys in some form.'

She busied herself with some green frogs and whispered as some twit flounced on the screen, 'It's a mix of nagging some elusive object and him loving you, absolute bloody fancy. All make-believe, but people love make-believe.'

After the movie was finished I told my mother he was all right. 'Although I think he had a wig.'

'Mr Darcy wasn't bald,' said my mother.

'Yes,' I said, 'but I think that fella's hair was a bit thin. But he was pretty good.'

My mother was silent for a while. 'Yes,' she said, 'I liked him, I liked that Mr Darcy.'

'Didn't there used to be a trotter called Mr Darcy?' I asked.

'No,' my mum corrected, 'I think it was a greyhound that belonged to Eddie Lippiatt.'

'Right.'

I felt light-headed; the hammer had done its work.

'Let's get some beer and prawns and watch some other Mr Darcys and compare.'

'I'd rather fix the gate,' I said.

'Well it's going to rain,' said my mother, 'so make yourself comfortable.'

The beer and prawns almost made the next two days bearable. Almost. First we watched Laurence Olivier and his Brylcreem at work.

'He was short but very funny,' was my mother's verdict.

Next was some old hazy video from the BBC in the sixites with a thin-lipped fellow with permed hair.

'Walks like he's done his knees.'

'He's all right,' I said. 'He's just a bloke who's trying to earn a living.'

'And you'd know?' my mother said.

I sat through Lizzy Bennets and Mr Bingleys, and balls and weddings and bonnets and more balls and even more Mr Bingleys. Mr Darcy bursting into libraries and declaring his love for Lizzy Bennet and then flouncing off like he had a feather duster up his Mr Arsey.

The beer almost got me through Colin Firth's turn. Nearly, but not quite.

We got to the bit where Col jumped in the water. 'Is that it?' I asked.

'Well what more do you want?' said my mother as she scratched her dog Blodwyn's stomach. 'Yes he's bit podgy and well-fed but he fills out those breeches nicely.'

'Well good on chubby Col,' I said as I sipped down a beer. 'He doesn't do much, does he? Just stands there and puffs out his cheeks.'

'You are a stupid boy. He doesn't have to do anything. That's the point of Mr Darcy. Anyway you can bloody talk!' my mum said as she squashed a flea between her fingers.

It was true. I had played Mr Darcy on stage once in Sydney and Melbourne in the nineties and the whole experience and those times flooded back to me on that wet weekend.

And I couldn't help but think that we'd all been sold lollies that weren't real, we'd all been sucking on falsies. We'd all been searching for Mr Darcys in some form, and just like my mum had said, we'd done all the work for a bit of make-believe.

After Paul Keating met his fate against John Howard in 1996 a certain vagueness drifted through the community. The former Queensland premier Wayne Goss had said that voters were waiting for Keating with baseball bats and after the bludgeoning they gave him it was as if everybody had to catch their breath a bit.

All Keating's big ticket items like a republic and closer ties to Asia, and his perceived dalliances with the finer, more esoteric points of the arts, had distanced him from the concerns of everyday Australians according to John Howard. It was funny that nobody in the long line of Australian politics has ever really set down what it is that the mythical everyday Australian family actually is and wants.

It's a floating concept that gets a great deal of play every time there is an election. And when a government has been in too long then they find it hard to find a form of everyday Australians that they haven't used before.

And how could you argue with Howard? He'd won and now he had to find something to do. He'd made a series of vague speeches of intent called 'headland speeches' but he'd been given a free ride into power on the back of the longevity of the Labor government Keating headed and its deep unpopularity.

During the election campaign I'd seen Keating at a rally for the arts.

He dragged himself into the bowels of the Victorian Arts Centre where people from the 'Arts' rallied for him. That basically meant a series of actors, singers and dancers getting up and talking about themselves. At the end somebody made sure they were in the spotlight and then in a breaking voice said, 'Mr Prime Minster, I don't think you realise just how much you are loved.'

An old man who used to be a judge on a talent quest said, 'What beautiful delivery,' as if he was awarding points to the night's winner.

Keating got to his feet and looked very tired. I think he had a pretty good idea of who loved him that year.

'When you change the government,' he said, 'you change the country.'

He meant it as a warning but it was taken as a big tip to the Australian people. They wanted a change and they got it.

For much of Howard's first term he had to find something to stand for. He muddled about with better codes of conduct for his ministers, which effectively meant he had to sack half of his cabinet for slack bookkeeping and travel allowances fibs. Or it seemed that way. Howard seemed to be a little bit at sea.

I had spent much of this time pretending to be someone else on a television show. The show was quite successful and would run for almost as long as Howard's term as prime minister. The Monday after he was elected I wandered into the studio and bumped into a hale and hearty network executive.

'Billy.' He nodded a greeting.

I nodded back.

'Fucking good result on Sat'day.' The hale and hearty one pushed a fist up into the air.

'You happy then?' I asked.

'Fucking deeeeelighted. A golden age, mate, fucking golden age.' And he went off whistling down the hallway while I dragged myself to a dressing-room and into my make-believe costume.

I never really knew if he was referring to Howard's victory or his football team. He barracked for Geelong. And I presume John Howard and the Liberals.

The television network made most of its money from sport, namely by broadcasting the Olympics and the football. The more money they paid each year for the rights, the more football was shown. It counted as Australian content after all. Blokey mates were being born anew, with well-paid, made-up mates in smart suits with little emblems of the station on the breast pockets, smiling and 'bloke-ing' on from the television screen.

Every second person you met in the station's corridor waddled along the way broken-down old football players do. It wasn't just footballers though, swimmers and runners, horsey folk and even old tennis champions loitered everywhere.

The importance they held was palpable, and the air was thick with sport. The Australian media were beginning to make sport a spectator event. It was no longer about being an actual participant in the game.

I was as guilty as any of opening my mouth and devouring whatever sport was being broadcast. One Sunday I was listening to the football as I drove, as was my custom. I shushed the singing of my young son in the back of the car so I could listen to what the commentator was saying. My team was playing and they were getting beaten, just.

My son started singing again and laughed a little as he sat in his booster seat.

'Shush! Daddy's trying to listen.' He was quiet as I listened to my team miss a shot for goal. I groaned and swore under my breath. I felt some sort of anger rage for a moment. I don't know why it really mattered if the Bulldogs won, but at that moment it seemed vitally important.

My son laughed at something and I shouted at him.

He was silent. I pulled over to the park where we were going to go for a walk. I decided I had to listen to the football for awhile longer. It was then I heard a change in the commentator's voice. His name was Peter Booth and he had a warm, pleasant voice with an idiosyncratic cadence to it.

'I don't know, I don't know, but I'm so sorry. We are hearing the most awful news from Tasmania.'

The voice that had shrieked moments before of missed opportunity and poor commitment to achieve the hard ball gets had vanished as he starkly told the story of what was unfolding in Port Arthur. While I was shouting at my son to stop his singing, lives were being ended at the hands of a gunman. Families were being ripped asunder by a lone act of madness.

'I don't know, I don't know how... it's just awful. These poor people. I suppose I'll have to go on, but these reports.'

The game went on and as the number of the dead went up in hideous correlation to the score of the football match I felt ashamed.

I felt ashamed. The pain in Peter Booth's voice made me switch the radio off. I looked at my son. He stared blankly at me. I took him from the car and held him very close. He kissed me on the cheek. What I did to deserve such a gift was beyond me.

I have always tried to remember that moment. It told me a lot about perspective and life.

John Howard pushed through a raft of gun ownership reforms and stood in a bulletproof jacket bulging beneath his suit at a gun owners' rally to plead his case. He was there and engaging in leadership.

'Who would ever have thought that an Australian prime minister would have to wear a bulletproof vest to a public meeting?' my mother said. It was chilling but this was the shadow of Port Arthur. This was Australia.

I watched Howard on the television news and I remembered something my father had once told me.

'There's Labor and Liberal, and right and wrong, but you'll know when you see someone do something right. You'll know it and it won't matter a tinker's cuss what brand the fella belongs to, you just know you back him up.'

Well John Howard earned his keep that day.

But it was what happened when he stopped muddling about and started running and running. And it seemed like he wouldn't stop. And it all started with The Don.

•

I was trying to take a photograph of my son's batting stance when I first heard Howard speak about Don Bradman being the greatest living Australian. The irony was not lost on me for I was engaged in a ritual that some fathers seem to happily follow from generation to generation. The formal portrait of the batting stance. I remember my father telling me to get out in the backyard and to face up with a five-star linseed-oil-covered Pakistani Christmas stocking filler for posterity. I've read enough bad cricket biographies to know that the copious photo pages in the middle of the book will undoubtedly contain such a shot of the book's subject with a caption pointing out that the future star cricketer had a remarkable stance even at the age of four.

The trick is to just take the photograph. Many a father has attempted to instruct and form the stance with the ancient art of yelling. But you have to accept what you have been dealt.

When my photo was taken by my mother, my father looked hard at me and was going to shout some advice but thought better of it and, as the saying goes, took it on the chin.

'Jesus, he's holding the bat like Bernard Bloody King! It's not a bloody feather duster. Oh well, has to be done. Take the photo, love.'

On reflection it is no wonder my batting stance didn't make the photo pages of a cricket biography.

Happily for me, my son held the bat in a suitably young tyro method and, after taking the snap, I called out, 'Good boy!' as if I had captured some rare scientific occurrence.

My son happily dropped the bat and went trailing after a butterfly in the garden while I listened to Howard bang on about Don Bradman, who was Howard's favourite cricketer as a boy. His favourite cricketer still, a hero to him then and a hero now.

Happily for Howard another nice little irony occurred. Kerry Packer, the man from Mrs Glazier's television who had bought cricket almost lock, stock and barrel in the 1970s, had also bought The Don in an exclusive interview. Bradman had been a member of the cricketing establishment whose parsimonious treatment of the 1970s cricketers had made Packer's ownership of the game possible. Now he was giving his time to Packer's network in return for a fee to help fund the Bradman museum.

The interview was watched by a staggering amount of people, and even though there can be little doubt that Howard's esteem and admiration for Bradman were sincere, it must be remembered that Howard was a politician, so when he saw an opportunity he took it.

Howard had come to power promising people an Australia where they could be relaxed and comfortable. The end of the century was in sight and ominous warnings about Y2K bugs were already beginning to circulate. There was a whiff of paranoia in the air.

Perhaps it was a case of people having had enough change. Of people needing to be told that there was worth and certainty in what they were. The pall of Port Arthur still hung in the air.

John Howard had tapped a vein in the Australian people and he was set to mine it for all he was worth.

My father had told me once that anybody who named Bradman as their favourite cricketer had no appreciation for the game. Bradman was, according to my father, as close to genius as the game could ever hope to have.

'There'll never be another Bradman and that's a good bloody thing. He was a machine. A winner with no personality. Always go with the fellow that's a little bit human. That's where the drama is, the action.'

My old man's favourite cricketers were Keith Miller and Stan McCabe and, despite his safari-suit episode, he always had time for Ian Chappell.

As I sat in my garden listening to Howard I thought of the prime minister's affection for Bradman.

Hawke had been the ultimate suburban sporting jock, whenever he appeared on the dais with some sporting champion you always had a sense that Hawke had some connection to what had occurred. But Howard added a whole new dimension. If Keating had been the biggest game in town with his theatre of sporting politics and his use of sledging, then Howard began moulding his connection to Australia by taking on the role of The Great Supporter.

He made no boast of his sporting prowess, indeed he couldn't wait to tell people he was a cricket tragic – no talent with the game but, just like a common man, he loved to watch. He was so normal.

Going by my father's reckoning you picked Bradman as your favourite player simply because he was the best. He was a winner. You picked him because of his success not because of his personality. Not because he didn't have one, simply because it wasn't an attractive one.

'It's not that the fella bites the heads off chooks,' my father said, 'it's just that he's a bit of a cold fish. So I suppose you'd like him just because he was the best.'

And it wasn't Bradman's fault that he suddenly became lionised and deified. He had probably wanted nothing more than to go about his business the way he always had, quietly and unobtrusively, paid due deference but out of the gaze of the public.

Now he had become a national obsession all over again. Bradman had belonged to an Australia of short haircuts, set loyalties and small horizons. The Australia that was proud, but proud of being British. I thought it was just a load of old guff. But perhaps that was the Australia that had formed John Howard. And a lot of other Australians.

There is a tendency to blame national leaders for all ills and spills, but the Australian people are never led anywhere where they themselves don't want to go. If nobody had watched Bradman's interview and Howard's remarks hadn't connected with people so much then perhaps it would all have gone away.

It didn't and Howard was up and running.

I walked the dog to the post office one morning and saw a kid walk off to the local school dressed up in his cricket whites. He had a made-up baggy green Australian cricket cap on his head.

'Good outfit,' I said.

'I'm The Don,' the boy said.

'Yeah.'

'Yeah.'

'It's heroes day at the school,' said a woman I took to be his mum. 'You know, when the kids get dressed up as famous Australians.'

This explained why I had seen another child dressed as Ned Kelly, with a heavy paper helmet and body armour made from a box which had held a television. 'Open this end' was still visible beneath the black paint. Ned Kelly had walked with a girl dressed in an old-fashioned Footscray jumper with a number three on the back. I think she was a Teddy Whitten.

I laughed and told the mother of Don Bradman that I had seen Ned Kelly and Teddy Whitten.

'Oh well you see them every year, but we thought Declan should go as somebody really important.'

Perhaps it was the way I looked at her. Really important?

'You know Don Bradman saved Australia from Depression. Gave people hope.'

I should have grasped the initiative and patented the name Bradman, or even better, 'The Don', for an anti-depressive medication, but I just nodded and half smiled.

'It's good the kids know a bit about the people who made us what we are today.'

I nodded again.

Bradman disappeared as a human being and the semi-deification of him well and truly began. The problem for Donald Bradman was that he became the subject of conjecture and debate. He probably was conservative, and maybe indulged in a bit of sectarianism and polite social prejudice. He was possibly quite elitist in terms of how he saw himself and his country, but then he wouldn't have been the only Australian of his generation who was like that.

For every person who thought he was responsible for saving us from Depression, discovering penicillin and inventing the automatic can-opener, there were people who labelled him a raging anti-Catholic, right-wing jackbooter.

It was a little sad.

'I suppose that's what they mean by the culture wars,' my mother said down the phone when I told her about it. 'The poor old fellow probably just wants to be left alone and all of a sudden they're putting him on stamps.'

I asked her what she thought of him.

'Tiny little man who was a bit too tidy for my liking. But he could play.'

Who was her favourite cricketer?

'Oh Richie Benaud by a mile. He was very glamorous, the way he used to wear his shirts unbuttoned to his ankles.'

Australia, it seemed, was changing.

I could tell that from where I worked, for I was occupying two worlds: I existed in Australia and I spent time pretending to inhabit the world of the telly show.

The most important day of the week for the cast was the rehearsal day. You'd be given your week's mail, your fan mail. People would sit around the set and go through the letters like researchers seeking the truth in ancient manuscripts.

The letters were usually just fun. People asking for an autograph and the like. Nothing to really write home about.

I hardly used to get any – a couple of loopy people from the back of beyond would write and invite me to go shooting with them but really that was about it. What I did like to do was to write fake fan mail to my other friends in the cast. It was a mild joke but so seriously were these forms of correspondence taken that they soon became my major form of entertainment.

My letters in disguise became so outrageously fawning and sycophantic that I was sure my co-workers would twig they were from me, indeed the letters all had the same postcode. But no, they really believed that a fan had written to them.

Being famous blinds you. You live in a bubble. It is a part of your job so you have to believe it to a certain extent. But the fact that otherwise sensible people who happen to be on the telly believe that small shrines are being built for them in Longreach and that people come and pray beside them for healing, or that sailors in the Royal Australian Navy write your name on ballistic missiles as a form of love and devotion, is a little sad.

It is also terribly human. The more famous you become, the more you look into yourself, the more you become the centre of your world. When that happens you lose irony. The world becomes very literal.

It is a simple way of going about your days and it is quite pleasant. And in a way that's what was happening to a lot of people right across the country.

People were beginning to take themselves terribly seriously.

One day in the studio, an old actor who had been around since Moses was a boy turned to me and grumbled when he heard that the studio monitors were being tuned to the Academy Awards ceremony to see if Geoffrey Rush was going to win the best actor award.

Rehearsals were forgotten as we crowded around the sets.

'Oh fuck,' said the old actor in his beautiful ex-radio voice. 'Why the bloody hell can't we just do this silly bloody thing and go home?'

'Don't you want to see if he wins?' I asked.

'Not particularly. Although I hope he does.'

The nominees were read out and more people came into the studio. The hale and hearty network executive was one of them.

'It's happening now, it's live,' Hale and Hearty said for no reason.

I thought of floating in a pool and the girl who could do handstands like Nadia Comaneci.

'Live via satellite,' I said slowly.

The old actor looked at me.

'Jesus, that's an old one.'

'It's hard to believe it's happening now, isn't it?' repeated Hale and Hearty to an actor from the television show.

'It's hard to believe we shared a dressing room once,' said a pleasant actor.

'He's in Hollywood and you're here!' Hale and Hearty laughed.

The pleasant actor nodded sadly.

Geoffrey Rush's name was read out and the studio erupted. People began clapping and cheering.

'Well played, son!' yelled Hale and Hearty.

'Bloody hell, that's good,' yelled another suit.

The old actor sighed.

'Not happy?' I asked.

'It's like everybody's got to pretend it's a game of fuckin' football. Look, I don't mind a punt, and God help me I'm a lifelong Tigers man, but it's the way you've got to pretend it's all a sport to belong. To make it more acceptable. To make sure you fit in, to be a good bloke. Like those galahs.' He pointed over to the executives.

'I think that's a bit much,' I said.

'Well good for fucking you then. I liked things when you could be what you wanted to be. What's the point of living in a democracy if you have to be like everybody else? You even have that bloody farce of a football game on Anzac Day. Why can't you just leave the bloody day for the people who earnt it? No, whack a bit of sport on, make it something more than it is. Oh for Christ's sake, can't we shoot this silly bloody thing?'

The old actor had a point. From the prime minister down sport was infiltrating everything. You didn't have to play sport to be a good bloke, to prove you were a real Australian, but you had to like sport.

Even Hollywood award ceremonies were placed in a sporting context to make them seem more Australian. It was an extension of the idea of being Australian, or rather of knowing what was unAustralian.

Where Bob Hawke had sat in his champagne-soaked blazer, John Howard sat in his comfortable chair in front of the telly, or the corporate box at the sporting events he attended. I don't think it was a case of John Howard manipulating people, it was more a case of him enjoying the view as he sailed along with the tide.

Once Bradman was elevated to 'National Defining Image' another icon was quickly added. Anzac Day.

The old actor was right. The day of homage had been taken to a new level. Anzac Day wasn't left alone for those who had earnt the right to march and remember. It was turned into an event for the wider community. Playing a 'blockbuster' footy match on one of our national days was indicative of how the broader community was engaging in owning the past. Or perhaps more accurately, enjoying the past.

The footy game was the icing on the cake of the rediscovery of Anzac Day that had begun in the eighties. Attendances at the dawn service at Gallipoli had gained popularity akin to a theme party.

A crew member spoke about how he had gone to the dawn service a year before. 'Great time. Unbelievable. I mean you can only take in so much booze but as long as you don't make a total arse of yourself the Mussies don't mind that much. And there was a heap of gunj available, so it was a top time. Pretty moving too. Great experience.'

Even little children had to come face to face with this new world.

My son had a friend. A nice boy. Lived up the road. They'd kick the footy to each other out in the street and discuss who should play where and who should play on whom. They're mates. They'd even ask themselves why they supported the same local footy team. Well, they both decided, they could change, but what was the point? They'd only be pretending. No, they were stuck with the Bulldogs.

So when I saw my son walking back down from his friend's house looking a little too quiet, I knew something was wrong. Maybe his friend had finally found a reason to barrack for another team, like Hawthorn. I called my boy over and asked him if everything was okay. He nodded. He nodded his head but he didn't look at me. So I got him to hand-pass the footy to me, so I could see his face.

'What's up?' I asked as he flipped me the ball.

'Just thinking,' he said.

'What about?' I sent the ball back.

'Things,' he said and he held the ball.

'Things. What sort of things?' I waited and asked him again. 'What sort of things?'

'Deniz… Deniz is my friend.' My son's face was beginning to flush. 'He's my friend. Will he be sad…will he get upset because of Anzac Day?'

Deniz is his friend from down the road. He is Turkish.

'What makes you think he'll get upset by Anzac Day?'

My boy looked up at me. A young face, completely open, without guile or malice. 'Why is it good we fought the Turkey people? Why is it good we bet them?'

It was hard not to laugh. We bet the Turkey people. We beat the Turkish people. My son was so earnest and sincere.

I realised that for the first time his little world of friendship and family had been intruded on by the grown-up world and its sense of history and pride.

'Well, first thing, we didn't bet the Turkey people. The Turks saw us off. They beat us. We attacked them and they saw us off. We had to retreat.'

And I felt sad. Sad because my son, who was just a little boy, had been fed a falsehood by a mood in our society. A mood of triumphalism. A need to say we won the war. We won. We were right. We have no reason to question or doubt our past, we won.

We passed the ball to each other. He found the fact that we were beaten awful. Then in his face a shadow. 'Why did we want to fight with them? Didn't they like the Anzacs?'

Where do you start to explain something that happened so long ago that you are not even sure of it yourself? But the effects of that event are still felt. To explain it to a young boy. To try to understand it yourself.

The power of Anzac Day is its sense of loss, of sacrifice. Of service. Its great emotional power is that each year the numbers that march become fewer. The very fact that the years of peace have meant that fewer and fewer people need to march is lost by many who seek to turn the Anzac tradition into some sort of ongoing industry. Those who march did their job. They made a lasting peace. I'm sure they are happy that their numbers shrink as time rolls by.

Anzac Day shouldn't celebrate war; it celebrates comradeship, and friendship. Service. It is about death and waste. It is about so many things. But is that the Anzac Day that we all celebrate? I kicked the ball to my son. It's a National Day. I suddenly felt that power of a national myth that can seep through all levels of society.

No one person creates it, it comes from some need in the society that believes it. But how do you explain that to a little boy. How do you explain the fact that you can buy sand from Gallipoli in authentic and official vials at the local post office? Did that make it any more real?

Is that what you had to have to appreciate what was done?

I did my best.

'Well people a long time ago fought so we could become a place where you and Deniz could be friends. Where we could be friends with the Turkey people. Where we could be a place where lots of different types of people can be friends.'

My son asked me if I had ever had to fight.

'No,' I said.

Would he have to fight?

'Well I hope not,' I said. I couldn't say anything else. It's one of those moments where as a parent you just don't know what to say. Awful thoughts race through your mind. And I felt suddenly quite angry. Angry at the way events are perpetuated with no account of consequence. If you celebrate stuff like Anzac Day without knowledge of the deeper sacrifice of life and the loss of those lives, the loss of all that possibility, then it seemed to me that flew in the face of what the whole thing was about.

So what did I do? Not much. Gave my son a cuddle and took him inside.

Not only had John Howard inherited an economy that had and reformed, his government had an ability to make it tick along quite nicely. He also inherited an Australia that was engaged in an encouragingly large amount of sporting success. A happy mixture for any government. Howard was a man who'd learnt a lot from his time in politics. He extended Bob Hawke's embracing of all things sporting and moulded it to suit his own qualities, and he took Keating's use of the sledge and tailored it to suit his own less pyrotechnical image. He called into question the Leader of the Opposition's ability to govern, simply by saying that Kim Beazley, 'Lacks the ticker for the hard decisions of government.'

It was such old-fashioned language, as if it were a line from *The Sullivans*. But it was effective. He said it with his considered, suburban solicitor tone and it found a willing audience. Kim Beazley was labelled as being an affable, intelligent windbag. Not a bad man, but just lacking a bit of backbone.

John Howard may have been many things but he didn't seem to lack political courage. He was more than willing to back himself and he went to the 1998 election with the unenviable platform of imposing a goods and services tax. The GST that had gifted Keating the 1993 election.

Howard managed to circumnavigate a scare campaign by cutting a deal with the wobbly leader of the Democrats Meg Lees, who sowed the demise of that party by agreeing to pass the GST in the Senate with a few adjustments. As the whole debate about the GST began, my time in the TV series was coming to an end.

I was leaving the halls of the network and, as was the wont when something important happened, we gathered in the loading bay to watch, live via satellite. As scenery was pushed in and sets changed we watched Pat Rafter play the final points of his US Open final. Hale and Hearty was there again with his bad tie and puffy shirt sleeves.

'Jeez, this is amazing. Economy going gangbusters and we're gong to have a tennis grand slam winner again. And,' Hale and Hearty paused, 'he is a top bloke, a real Aussie. Fantastic. Good old-fashioned name too, that helps.'

As Pat Rafter won the final point and smiled, he did indeed look like a good bloke. Cheering broke out in much the same manner as when Geoffrey Rush had won his Academy Award.

We all looked up at Rafter and somebody said, 'God, he must feel fantastic. He looks so happy.'

It was then that Hale and Hearty said something that summed up so much about television and men and sport, and human existence.

'Mate, he's got free head jobs for a year. Well played, Pat.' I looked at Hale and Hearty and saw that he was deadly serious.

It really was time to move on.

•

'Where are you at with your riding, Bill?' a friendly cowboy asked as I sat perched up on a big, healthy looking horse.

'Well I don't think I'll fall off if it stands still.'

The cowboy looked at me and summed up the situation. 'Right, you are fucking nowhere with your riding. Right.'

It wasn't supposed to come to this. After having left the TV series, I had travelled to the Northern Territory in a plane with an entertainment channel that played songs from a series of performers who had all died in plane crashes. This was never mentioned directly but was alluded to with insinuating whispers by the host that, 'That was a song from another late great who left us too early.'

Patsy Cline, Buddy Holly, The Big Bopper, Otis Redding, Jim Croce and even the Japanese guy who sang a song that some club singer from the sixties turned into a ballad about the Australian boxer Lionel Rose. With every new song I started becoming a little more anxious. I couldn't stop humming the one the Japanese guy sang.

I knew he died because I was listening to it once at a barbeque and Aunty Rita said, 'That's the song by the Japanese fellow who was on a plane that flew into Mt Fuji.'

My mother said that it wasn't a Japanese fellow singing. 'He doesn't sound Japanese.'

'That's a different fellow.'

'Why would a Japanese fella sing a song about Lionel Rose?' said my father.

'He'd sing a song about Fighting Harada if he was a Japanese fellow,' said Uncle Reg.

'It's a song that was based on a Japanese fellow's song. The Japanese fellow who flew into Mt Fuji. This fellow is some Sri

Lankan chap pretending to be P.J. Proby. The fellow who split his pants. You know P.J. Proby.'

'Is that why he flew into Mt Fuji, cause he split his pants?' said my father.

It was a slightly unnerving flight to say the least. But not as unnerving as seeing the man who was supposed to double for me in the film project I was a about to embark upon.

It was to be a great Australian outback film, as so many films are supposed to be – but it all went downhill very quickly. Especially when I saw the double. His legs were so bandy that a beer barrel could be rolled through them and he was lucky if he was five feet five – and that was in his cowboy boots.

So I found myself on a horse. All six foot four and fifteen stone of me. Behind me were about a thousand head of cattle that I was supposed to be droving across the outback for some reason. The pleasant director wandered over and asked me if I was watching the debate tonight between Beazley and Howard. I said I would be if a television could be found.

'That fella Howard has got it all worked out,' said the cowboy. 'He's got this debate and he's got the Commonwealth Games, where we are gonna win a shitload of medals, and we've got all of the footy finals and no bugger will want to know about any bloody election. He's a clever bugger.'

I nodded, Howard certainly had timed his election well.

'Now, Bill, when I tell you to go, hang on to them reins and swing that whip like you know what you are doing.' The cowboy smiled.

I nodded. The director yelled 'Action' and all the cows behind me started to moo, then they started to bellow and then the ground began to tremble a little.

'Look around, William, and then ride off,' cried the friendly director.

I looked around in my best outback horseman mode and nearly shat myself.

A thousand big bellowing cows were clumping toward me.

I was about to scream when the cowboy, hidden behind a little clump of bushes, sprang up, lifted the horse's tail and pinched the gee-gee where no gee-gee should ever be pinched. The horse took off like a rocket and I held on for dear life.

'Go, son, go! Wave that whip, Bill, wave that whip!' screamed the cowboy.

I flung the whip like a lunatic, back and forth until I thought my arm would leave my shoulder. I whipped myself in the face and I whipped the horse on the arse and that made the poor thing just go faster.

One of the crew swore I screamed something about Mt Fuji and Lionel Rose but for my own part I had no memory. I stopped somewhere up near Indonesia.

'By Christ! Some of that might be useable,' muttered the director.

The scriptwriter asked the friendly director why I was yodelling.

'I think he was screaming.'

'My hero shouldn't scream. He should look like Randolph Scott and *he* never yodelled,' said the scriptwriter definitively.

In the end, none of it could be used. It wasn't so much that the cows turned out to be a breed that hadn't been introduced into Australia until decades after World War I when the film was supposed to be set. It was that all the animals had large circular green plastic tags hanging from their ears. They looked like they were wearing earrings.

I was supposed to be an ex Light Horseman.

'They'd need a team of them fuckin' Clydies that pull them beer barrels to get you from go to whoa, Billy,' said the cowboy. 'You are a whole lot of ham up there, matey.'

It didn't get much better. But everybody meant well.

There was the novelty of having four sets of caterers who all thought that someone else was going to do the cooking. The most entertaining of all was a group of crocodile hunters whose cook was a certifiable ex sub-mariner who had a habit of dropping the blocks of hash he kept in his top pocket into the porridge or the soup he was cooking.

They disappeared after the first couple of days. Then there was one of the actors who had forgotten his Prozac, which meant that it was like Dr Jekyll and Mr Hyde on set.

A group of broken-down old rodeo riders and drovers followed everybody around because the producer was a friend of theirs and had decided that they could be in the film, or be technical advisers.

I was taught to crack a whip and then given a bottle of rum to drink by one of these technical advisers. They were amazing men who had spent years in the outback, winding their lives along the stock trails and emptiness of the country. They were were walking bits of history from another century.

They also quoted ad nauseam the most banal poems and songs that ever rhymed along the range.

The film was supposedly a story of Indigenous Australians and Europeans, but it was more like a beautiful dream which never quite saw the light of day.

'Well it wouldn't be the first time that dream died out here,' drawled a drover. 'Dare say it won't be the last.'

The emptiness of the landscape was desperate at first. I felt so alone. The sense of timelessness that people had spoken of, and I had dismissed as tripe, was too palpable. But then it became reassuring. The beauty of that timelessness was quite humbling.

It struck me that the idea of ownership of such a land was a quaint idea because it was all too apparent that we were simply passing through.

It wasn't until I got to places like Tennant Creek and the camps around Alice Springs that I saw just how much had been lost and just how far the gap in the idea of being Australian had grown. I had great stabs of sadness of what had happened to the people who had been in these lands before European settlement. About how fellow Australians were living now.

I told an old stockman who had taught me how to crack a whip about these great stabs of sadness.

He had a brown wrinkled face and eyes that were sunken beneath lines from too many days riding into the sun.

'Well now, what do you think you'll do about it?' he said softly.

I shrugged my shoulders.

'That's about the size of it. Lost something, that's for certain. It's a funny thing, we all claim things that happened that make us feel good. Them Anzac fellows and the like. But we'll shut up shop when somebody asks for a bit of responsibility for what's happened. Not talking about guilt. Just talking about owning our history...weak as piss really.'

He was silent for a long time and then he said with a sigh, 'Well maybe there's not much point. We're all just passing through...all of us.'

Election night was held in Coober Pedy. A race meeting was also held that night. So I left my hotel room and went out to enjoy a bit of local nightlife.

I had a meal in a café that had a sign over the door requesting patrons not to eat with dynamite on their persons.

'Just there for the tourists, matey. Playing up to our past.' The waiter winked.

The town did seem to engage in a little bit of role-playing.

'More unsolved deaths out here per capita than in New York,' a man who ran a petrol station had told us as we filled up one of the crew vehicles. 'Lots-a holes out there with lots-a people down the bottom. Well, that's what I read somewhere...once.'

Playing up to our past to turn a profit. Just bunging on a show. I suppose we all did it.

At the post-races 'ball' lots of drunken people wearing cowboy hats and big boots were waltzing about. I sat drinking at a makeshift bar and a huge cowboy staggered up to me and asked me if I had a light.

I looked at him and shook my head.

The crown of his big black hat was on fire. He staggered off and bellowed for a light. He returned moments later and asked me again.

'Your hat is on fire.'

He stared at me.

'Your hat,' I repeated pointing to his head.

He stood as still as he could and then slowly took the hat from his head, looked at it and slowly bent his mouth toward the flaming hat and lit his smoke. He banged the hat on the ground and the flame expired. He put it back on his head and it looked like he had a small smoking volcano on the top of his large person.

He drew in on his cigarette, exhaled and then smiled. 'It's hard to believe a silly prick like me helped choose the government today. But you know, we get the government we deserve.' He touched the brim of his smoking hat and lurched off laughing.

I went back to the hotel in time to see the concession and victory speeches. Howard lost a lot of seats and looked a little grumpy, and Beazley looked jolly and happy. He hadn't won.

'He looks relieved more than anything else,' said one of the crew.

'Maybe he was too soft.'

'No,' said the director of photography. 'He's a man who thinks too much. He'll never be prime minister. We're stuck with Howard.'


A little over one year later, as well as having John Howard as prime minister, Australia had two World Cup winning teams – one in Rugby and one in cricket – a constitutional referendum and some boofhead play-acting Jane Austen at the Sydney Opera House.

I had managed to behave myself in Melbourne. But when I got to Sydney I'm afraid I gave up the ghost somewhat. A few hotdogs and dim sims here and there, the odd beer with friends and the idea that Mr Darcy had turned into Mr Arsey.

In front of the television during that wet *Pride and Prejudice* weekend years later my mum helpfully reminded me of this fact, 'My god you were the size of a zeppelin.'

'Mum, I think you're stretching things a bit.'

'When you wore those boots and that coat you were the size of a block of housing commission flats.'

'Well,' I said in a considered voice, 'I was referred to as a great brown-trousered egret by somebody I admire.'

'Who?' said my mother.

'My wife,' I said.

'Knew I liked the girl for a reason.'

We laughed. We were, I think, both delirious.

It was, though, sadly true. My costume hardly fitted me and I looked more like Mr Rochester on a bad day with one too many visits to his mad wife up in the attic.

It wasn't helped by the fact that the whole production was unimaginably successful. Stomping around looking like a fat grump in clothes that didn't really fit didn't seem to make any difference.

I would leave the Sydney Opera House after I had finished pretending to be the richest man in Netherfield, or wherever the bloody thing was set, to wait for a bus to take me back to my mattress on a friend's floor.

I would stumble like some unmade bed along the harbour around Circular Quay and sometimes I would be stopped by people, usually American tourists who had just seen the show.

'Oh we loved it. What a lovely story.' They were big and pale and scrubbed clean, and they reminded me of the Americans who had wandered the streets of Perth.

What they made of the republic referendum that was going on at the time was anybody's guess. I think they thought we were still just a part of Great Britain.

I remember standing out on the forecourt of the Opera House playing cricket in full costume as Mr Arsey with some of the theatre mechanics, as we often did during that production – as if a bit of sport was an antidote to the regal Georgian frippery we were earning our living in – and looking across Sydney Harbour to Kirribilli House, the prime minister's Sydney residence.

Since John Howard refused to use the Lodge in Canberra as his prime ministerial residence, he had use of a prime piece of Sydney waterside property instead. I thought of him, how he would be sitting down to a cup of tea in his mansion by the harbour.

Me dressed up as Mr Arsey and him and our referendum. Or his really. It was conceived in such a way that a 'Yes' vote in favour of a republic was never really likely. Howard had effectively split the pro-republican movement between those who had wanted the minimalist model with a head of state elected by the Federal Parliament of Australia, and those who wanted a popular vote by the people of Australia to choose the head of state. Perhaps he had some suspicions about how unpopular politicians could be painted to people in the country and there was an abroad that as a group the politicians would hijack the election of the head of state as their own private right.

I was joined by a member of the cast as I gazed across the harbour.

'Thinking about Howard?' he said, lighting a smoke.

I nodded.

'What I don't get about monarchists is that they will win this thing. And they're all such ugly-looking people. Out of work country singers and weird-looking lawyers from the North Shore.'

'Mate, that's a bit harsh.'

'Maybe, but fuck 'em – they're going to win.'

Not for the first time I thought we sounded like we were talking about sport. All year had been about sport and the two teams that won the world cups had been fêted and lionised by the press and the public alike.

Australia had won the Cricket World Cup and the Rugby World Cup before, but never at the same time.

Both these victories were portrayed as examples of the never-say-die Aussie spirit. The 'Anzac spirit' was mentioned more than once.

And I had bought into it, led by our nation's cheerleader at whose house we were looking.

John Howard had started wearing Australian paraphernalia on his morning walks around the streets.

It looked slightly ridiculous but it didn't seem to be doing him any harm. Perhaps it even added some subliminal message about sport and health and vibrancy to the prime minister's appeal.

All I know is that I joined in the triumphalism.

We had sat in the green room of the Opera House late one night after a performance to watch South Africa play Australia's Wallabies in a semi-final. We stayed well past the time we should have and a security guard came to kick us out.

'You lads right? Green room is closed.'

'Come on, mate, we're just watching the Rugby, cut us a bit of slack.'

The security guard looked at us and looked directly at me.

'Bob Dwyer or Alan Jones?' he said. He was asking me for an opinion on two former Australian coaches, both bitter rivals.

'Mate, I'm a Queenslander…can I go Bob Templeton?'

He smiled slightly. 'Bob Dwyer or Alan Jones?' he said again.

'Bob Dwyer,' I said.

'Pass, friend. Just make sure you nick off when the game's finished.' He smiled and moved off on his rounds.

I can still hear the sound that Steve Larkham's boot made on the ball when he kicked the drop kick to win the match with a field goal.

On my way to a matinee performance of *Pride and Prejudice* I noticed that there were more people on the streets than usual. Somebody told me it was a crowd for the Wallabies' street parade. I stayed for most of the parade and completely lost track of where I was supposed to be. I had already got my times mixed up with the daylight saving changeover and, on consideration, perhaps I stayed a little too long.

I cheered as loud as anyone there and when I saw a Queensland player I stood like a loon and bellowed, 'Queenslander!'

David Wilson even gave me a thumbs up.

I was a happy man when I made my way through the bowels of the Opera House and into the world of Jane Austen. I turned down a hallway and saw all the characters from *Pride and Prejudice* sitting in a group waiting for me.

'Bit keen are we?' I asked innocently, impressed that everybody was ready so soon.

A few of my friends giggled. This is when I knew something was up.

'Are you aware we have a performance at one o'clock?' asked a stage manager.

I should have apologised, I know, and I made sure I did to everyone later. But I had just seen the World Cup Wallabies. And David Wilson had given me the thumbs up.

I raised my fist in salute and yelled, 'Queenslander!'

That year's sporting success by Australian teams seemed to reinforce all the old ideas of our country. The end of the century was upon us and it was the sports of old Australia – the cricket and Rugby – the Anglo sports, the Commonwealth sports that had caught the public's eye. The sports by which we had measured our worth against the mother country, against England, by which we identified ourselves. Perhaps it gave us comfort to think that even though time was passing things didn't have to change. Maybe all countries need time to take a breath and relax. Maybe.

Even The Don reared his head. In Pakistan the affable Australian cricket captain Mark Taylor had scored an amazing 334 runs in a test match. On the last ball of the day he had equalled the highest score by an Australian, Don Bradman. He had the next day to outscore Bradman and grab his own piece of history, perhaps even the highest individual score.

I was in a supermarket checkout lane the morning he would decide what to do.

'I hope he goes on and gets the record,' said an Indian man in front of me.

'He's a lovely lad, bit chubby, but a lovely lad,' said an old lady behind me.

'My dad said he might declare so he wouldn't show up The Don,' said a girl on the cash register. She didn't look old enough to have finished high school and she spoke about The Don.

'He wouldn't do that,' I said.

'Well my dad said he would,' said the girl.

Her dad was right. Taylor declared. Whether he did so in honour of The Don or to pursue victory didn't really matter. It was as if the past and the icons it held weren't to be challenged; they were to be honoured.

But sport wasn't just a new method of politics. It didn't have to be something you sat down and watched, or something everyday people didn't do. You didn't have to be a professional to ply passion on the field. That's how I ended up outside a pub in Camden.


I walked out from the pub and the air rolled over me like a cool wave. And just for a moment I had that clarity that comes fleetingly when you've had a bit too much to drink. Outside the crowded pub I looked at the bloke spinning slowly like a Hills hoist in the breeze.

'Hey, Bill, they threw me out. I got thrown out of a pub! What do you think of that, Bill? Hey? What do you think of that?' He spoke with both his arms outstretched.

I looked at him and nodded. He seemed like a nice bloke. I'd met him earlier in the day and we'd had a chat and a drink, and I'd looked with surprised interest at the ants that crawled out of the crack in his arse.

We two, along with thousands of others across Australia, had been engaged in the torrid sporting contest known as Golden Oldies Rugby. Almost every weekend the green fields where the running game is played witness a peculiar demonstration of the fine art of ancient Rugby.

Ancient Rugby. That morning as I packed my kit bag, my niece had looked at me with a degree of trepidation.

'Uncle Bill, you and Dad won't hurt yourself will you? Playing Rugby?'

Before I could answer my sister-in-law laughed.

'Oh, I don't think so, darling. Dad and Uncle Bill aren't really playing Rugby, they're playing Golden Oldies.'

'Oh come on,' I said. 'Golden Oldies display skills long thought lost to the game.'

My niece stared at me.

'Fair dinkum,' I assured her.

'Oh, Uncle Bill,' my sister-in-law chided. 'What skills would they be?'

I looked at her and knew she was right. 'All right, old fat guys hugging each other. That's it.'

'Well, still, don't you get hurt,' said my niece.

Getting hurt was the furthermost thing from the contestants' minds as we paused for team photos. Basically because players had already started to imbibe in the therapeutic pain-killing drinks provided by the big esky under the tent.

It was a warm day and lots of drinks began to disappear as the sides mustered beneath the blue skies of Camden. And what sides they were.

The home team, the mighty Camden Withered Rams, was playing host to the wily and cunning Wagga Boiled Lollies.

So cunning and wily were the Boiled Lollies that, as they stood in their blue and white footy jerseys, I saw that they had half the Camden Withered Rams playing for them.

'Just had a few troubles getting a full complement,' said a tall boiled lolly puffing on a port cigar and nursing an Old in his wily, boiled lolly hands.

Looking around at the man-flesh that filled out the respective jumpers we were a true complement of Golden Oldies.

A Golden Oldie has to be over thirty-five. A gut is optional, though expected. It is also expected that port will be downed and that an elaborate inflation of the player's skill will be loudly declared to anyone within shouting distance.

Just like Banjo Paterson's poetry, 'all the cracks had gathered to the fray'. I don't think I have ever seen more tradesmen's canyons on display as we Golden Oldies heaved ourselves into our shorts. Man boobs to the fore, bad knees clanking in time with the grinding of our ankles, we marched onto the field in a procession that was comfortingly familiar from the opening credits of the old television comedy *Dad's Army*.

Angus La Good, gentleman farmer, general bon vivant and legend of Camden Rugby, welcomed everybody with a wave of his epically dislocated fingers and three mighty sheep calls and then it was on. I swear that Ray Crossley played the first minute or so in his vintage VIY's sunglasses. I could see myself reflected in something when I tried to tackle him.

Dave Mundy threw a dummy to nobody and got a round of applause.

'I threw one! I threw a dummy!' Caught on the bottom of a ruck he looked up at me. 'Now I can die happy.'

Conversations were carried out on the bottom of rucks, mauls and even in scrums.

'Shit, you've let yourself go, Ray,' said Dick Old.

'And it's all for you, baby,' replied Ray warmly.

During one scrum someone from the Boiled Lollies started to sing a song from the seventies band Racey, 'Lay Your Love on Me'. This was immediately answered with a salvo from the Withered Rams second row of the George Baker Selection's 'Paloma Blanca'.

Rugby played to the soundtrack of old K-Tel *Ripsnorter* albums. This was ancient Rugby at its fiercest.

We wandered off and stayed in the tent for hours, setting down some more legendary tales for future generations.

Back in the clubhouse a bit of money was raised for a local charity and a lot of fun was had. As the sun was setting the cigar-smoking Wagga Boiled Lolly felt compelled to display his arse as we drank in Golden Oldie comradeship.

It was a bizarre moment, partly because his display produced a tattooed image of big green ants crawling from his arse crack.

He hoisted his trousers back up and sauntered back to his table.

'Nice tatts,' I said.

'Yeah. Oh you know I was in the navy once.'

What that explained I don't really know but I nodded back. 'Yeah, mate.'

It was obvious that too much enjoyment was being had and that is why the Golden Oldies, the pride of Camden and Wagga, found ourselves at a crowded pub. Too much fun can be worse than none at all, which is why I had stepped out of that pub and found myself on the street in the cool night air being confronted by the Wagga Boiled Lolly with the ants crawling from the crack in his arse.

'What do you think, Bill?' he said.

What did I think? I nodded and looked at him.

All the images of the day raced through my mind.

'Mate,' I said.

'Yeah?' said the Boiled Lolly.

'Mate, Rugby was the winner today.'

'Too right,' said the Boiled Lolly.

On the night of the referendum it didn't take very long to work out who the winner would be. Not one state voted in favour of the republic model. Not one. In a move that displayed how elite and clubbish the republican campaign had been, a great marquee had been set up on the forecourt of the Sydney Opera House to hold the supposed victory celebration.

The thought would have been to let the echoing cries of joy and happiness of the new republic float across the Harbour to Kirribilli where John Howard would choke on his Horlicks.

Instead, we couldn't play cricket. And a merchant banker called Malcolm Turnbull rose to speak on behalf of all those Australians who had voted for and supported the 'Yes' vote, like myself. He had to put up with the vision of lots of people from Netherfield and Pemberley and all the other Austen hang-outs staring at him through the crowd of miserable republicans.

Most of the cast had wandered out and stood at the back of the marquee to see Turnbull and his large, indignant chin wobble and, in his best lawyer's voice, proclaim, 'That whatever else John Howard achieves as prime minister, history will remember him for one thing. He was the prime minister who broke this nation's heart.'

•

Well that was then. Did it really break the nation's heart? Life went on, as did the play. And by the time I made my way back along the harbour to Circular Quay the big marquee was all but empty.

But there were still lots of tourists about.

I could see them approach me and I could see they were American.

'Oh you're from the play. Oh, it was wonderful. And it was such a thrill for us to see your play in your opera house. Your play. It was so wonderful and romantic. You're lucky you have got such a wonderful culture, all that history you have. Could we have a photo?'

I could have told them that it wasn't my history. I could have told them 'our history' was something they had no idea about. But I remembered the old stockman's words. And I nodded and posed for a photo that they probably don't even know why they took.

I was like most Australians. I was just passing through.

'We're all just passing through,' I said to myself as I sat in my mother's house.

'What are you saying?' she asked.

'Nothing.'

'The rain's stopped, dear,' she said.

'Right,' I said and went back to the gate. I dubbed the sander Mr Bingley because he became my best friend. And the fucker never worked. Somehow I managed to fix the gate. I'm not quite sure how but, between rainstorms, it turned out okay.

I proudly displayed my handiwork to my mum. She was impressed. 'Well done,' she said as she gave me a pat. 'I like happy endings,' she told me.

'Yes, I know,' I said.

'Just like *Pride and Prejudice*.' She laughed.

I groaned and went for another beer.

# 9

I had a football coach once, a large red-headed man with a vast beard, foul temper, a daytime occupation as a Maths teacher and a tendency to scream out, 'What doesn't kill you makes you stronger! Stronger! STRONGER!'

When he was on song you could ask him the time, 'What's the time, Swede?'

And he would scream, 'What doesn't kill you makes you stronger! Stronger! STRONGER!'

'Thanks for that.'

I thought of him one Saturday morning as I sat at the boys shot-put at Little Athletics helping marshal the under-tens.

My marshalling partner was a man of about sixty and when the tribe of under-tens walked towards the pit he mumbled, 'Here they come...twelve years I've been doing this. Twelve years.'

It is a quaint idea 'marshalling' fifteen under-ten boys at the shot-put pit. They climb, pick, pull, punch and crawl over each other and listen to nothing anyone has to say.

Little Athletics makes three hours stretch into a decade.

'Its all about the kids,' said a too jolly woman about what we were doing.

'Twelve years,' said my partner in the pit.

'What doesn't kill you make you stronger! Stronger! STRONGER!'

I laughed grimly for I remembered hearing that the Swede had to give teaching and coaching away because he'd suffered a nervous breakdown, or ten. He ran a coffee shop and art gallery now.

Well, whatever doesn't kill you.

An under-ten picked up a small shot-put and decided to throw it at another competitor.

'Don't! Put it down – DOWN. Thank you.' I think it was his mother speaking. She turned and smiled. 'He's so keen.'

I looked at my partner.

'Twelve years,' I said.

He nodded and smiled grimly. 'Twelve and counting.'

My daughter sat in line with a group of girls at the long jump, playing a handclapping game.

There were children everywhere. My partner cleaned the pit and mumbled, loud enough so I could hear, 'It's no good trying to think of a way to make it go any faster. We'll get there, it's just what it is. Anyway, they're just being kids.'

He was right, it seemed like chaos but the morning passed and the kids ran, jumped and threw and they seemed to like it. And why not?

The older man came close to laughing. 'Kids have been behaving like this since we jumped out of the trees and that's longer than twelve years.'

It's pretty elemental. To run and to jump and to throw. To swim. To climb. I could see it would appeal to our prehistoric forebears as much as it does today.

The older man called out some names and the little faces turned and picked noses in his direction. Little bodies that belonged to Ryan and Thomas and co got up and stood awkwardly in line to throw the shot-put.

Behind them a line of teenage girls hared around the racetrack. My daughter was still handclapping. She threw back her head and laughed as her friend and her mucked up a routine.

Then the great blaring horn of a cargo ship called across the morning as the vessel slowly crawled along the river to the docks of Melbourne.

Its steady progression through the morning reminded me of a great prehistoric beast. And then much more. It reminded me of another boat with other people running and jumping around.

The year after the constitutional referendum was followed by the Sydney Olympics and John Howard, myself and countless thousands of others followed as well.

John Howard seemed to be everywhere.

He took Tom Joading to a whole new level. Wherever there was a medal to be won, there he was. It was when I saw him at the final of the women's water polo, when Australia beat the United States after the bell, that I thought conspiracy junkies would have a field day.

A game that normally would hardly rate a mention was all of a sudden the centre of the universe. Not for the first time

I was struck by how sports that are rarely seen on prime-time television screens provoke excitement and emotion during the Olympics. Is it because they are wonderful spectacles? Or is it because their moment in the national sun comes during the apex of national pride, Olympic success? A nose-picking competition would pull an audience if enough people thought there was a gold medal in it.

Yet, watching the water polo, I found myself shrieking in delight and jumping up and down in front of the television. A victory after the bell! Against the United States! Even if they are our great and powerful friends it's impossible not to like it when the United States get their comeuppance on the sporting field.

The camera swept around the applauding audience and stopped on cue to a clapping, happy Howard, Janette beside him.

It was a moment, only a moment, and then it went and was replaced by the realisation that that was what prime ministers did. Well, where else is he supposed to be, I asked myself. It's the Olympics. He's the head of the nation, of course he should be there. At the water polo.

The Olympics saw the height of Howard's role as chief supporter. The height of him as the everyman of sports-loving spectators.

The Olympics were all about being a spectator, although there were many different ways to be a part of it all. As I found out when I was invited to stay on a yacht in Sydney Harbour for a few days during the Olympics. The invitation came from the head of the network broadcasting the games, and I suppose if you are going to accept an invitation from a media magnate you might as well go to a yacht on the harbour.

When I turned up I realised that there are yachts and then there are yachts. This one was the size of a battleship. It was parked just under the Sydney Harbour Bridge and seemed as tall as the buildings that surrounded it.

I was welcomed and invited to be a part of the Sydney Olympics, or more accurately, to share the Olympic spirit.

The crew were all polite and wore uniforms like something out of a Gilbert and Sullivan operetta. The officers were even better, they all sported the most amazing accents, as if they were actors in an MGM musical from the 1950s. Everything seemed to be in glorious technicolour. I half expected the crew to start singing at the tops of their voices.

Before being shown to my cabin I was taken to meet my host, the media magnate. He was relaxing in shorts and sandals in a chair surrounded by some of his executives.

'Hello, welcome to the Olympics. Hope you enjoy yourself,' said the pleasant media magnate.

Over his shoulder I saw a familiar face give me a thumbs-up signal. It was Hale and Hearty and he looked as flush as any imbiber of the Olympic spirit. I nodded my thanks to the pleasant media magnate and said that I would do my best to enjoy my stay.

'Well it shouldn't be too hard, William,' said an executive.

'Think you'll survive it!' added another.

I laughed and then a shiver went through me.

'Yes, well, what doesn't kill you makes you stronger,' said the pleasant media magnate.

'Stronger! STRONGER!' I said, like an idiot.

He looked at me from behind his glasses and half smiled.

'Yes,' he said in his pleasant media magnate tone, but his eyes looked like they were examining a bug through a microscope.

I scuttled off to my cabin and was welcomed by the sight of two huge bottles of bourbon and gin. The MGM officer smiled and said, 'Of course-a you will be-a stayink only for a few-a days-a, and you-s welcome to your-a drinks-a. But you-are-a notta allowed-a to take-a the bottles-a with you. Your challenge-a!' He smiled and bowed.

With that, he was gone.

The ship was packed with people. The lower two decks had been hired by a huge American oil company so from the little balcony on my cabin I could look down and see a variety of Arabic headdresses, cowboy hats and baseball caps engaging in conversations.

The only problem was that occasionally the balcony doors seemed to lock shut, and distress calls in a multitude of accents would float up and along the hull of the ship.

One evening a man with a harsh loud voice called for help and I stuck my head out and called down to him.

'Locked out?'

'Yes, locked out!' he bellowed back.

Other people poked their heads out over their balconies.

'Hello!' sang out an old lady from America. 'Hello, are you okay?'

'Yes, locked out,' cried the man again.

'Oh those doors!'

'Yes, locked out!' The man said again. I don't think his English was that extensive.

That night I had taken up the challenge from the MGM officer concerning the Olympic spirits. Not too much, but enough to want a bit of fun.

'His doors are shut,' I said to the old lady.

'Yes, locked out... Locked out!' bellowed the man.

'Oh those doors...has anybody rung the crew?'

'I don't know,' I said.

'You rang the crew, mate?' I asked the man.

'Yes, locked out.'

The American lady called out somebody's name and then turned into her cabin. Then she called out to the man below, 'We're just ringing the crew.'

'Yes...' There was a pause.

'Won't be long,' said the American lady.

'Locked out!' came the bellow.

'Oh I don't think he has much English.'

'No.' I had a sip of bourbon. 'You enjoying the games?'

'Oh very much so,' said the American lady. She had a nice voice and was very polite, the way that lots of Americans can be.

'You have a beautiful country. So lovely. You really are wonderful hosts.'

'Locked out!' the man bellowed.

'Oh the poor man...' The American lady said how lucky she felt to have seen the opening ceremony. 'It's about as much as I've ever learnt about Australia.'

'Oh yes,' I said. 'What did you learn?'

She laughed. A nice laugh.

'Oh now, you'll just tease me... Well, how you all came here from across the seas, I never realised that about you. How so many of you come from so many different places...just like the States. My husband said I would like Australians. He said that you were a little rough but were very generous.'

'Oh a bit rough!' I laughed

'Locked out!' sang the man.

'They won't be long,' she said to the man, then turned back to me. 'Yes, but that was a long time ago. He told me that over fifty-six years ago. Well, he didn't tell me, he wrote me. From New Guinea.'

New Guinea? From her age I took him to be a veteran of World War II perhaps.

'Yes...he was a soldier, well he was a sort of soldier. He was a doctor. Although he did look handsome in his uniform. He just laughed when I told him so. He had the loveliest laugh so I kept on telling him he looked handsome.'

'Has he seen some changes?' I said. 'Hope we're not as rough as we were!'

She didn't answer.

I repeated what I said.

'Yes, locked out!' bellowed the man.

The American lady finally spoke.

'Oh he died...in New Guinea. He died not long after he wrote me...about what he thought about you people. You know, the last person he spoke to was probably an Aussie and somehow I always thought I should come here one day. I'd like to find out for myself. So here I am.'

There was silence.

I said I was sorry.

She told me not to be.

'You have a beautiful country and you are a so very generous people.'

From somewhere in some other cabin came a cry, 'Aussie, Aussie, Aussie!'

'Yes, locked out!' cried the man on the balcony.

And then an answering cry, 'Oi, Oi, Oi!'

Thankfully the crew came and opened the man's door.

'Thank you... Thank you,' said the man and he laughed.

'Oh well, you're welcome,' said the nice American lady.

'Dear, oh dear, but it's a beautiful night. Goodbye now.' And she turned into her cabin.

I looked out into the night. I seldom thought of the sacrifices other people and other countries had made. How many lost hopes and dreams. Of men with lovely laughs. Well, I don't suppose that many of us do, even if we are a generous people.

I drained the drink and went to go into my cabin.

The fucking door was locked.

Well, whatever doesn't kill me.


Of the games themselves, I can remember only vast crowds, the uniforms of the volunteers and the expanse of corporate catering tents with their brand names, banks of televisions and faces flowing with the Olympic spirit. And the blur of images of a night at the track.

I can't remember seeing anybody at the Olympic shot-put pit but I am sure they would have behaved in a more professional, but slightly less character-filled way than the under-tens.

The men's hundred metre relay was won by the Americans and the muscled, lycra-suited supermen posed and pointed in celebration. Someone in the crowd said loudly, 'The steroids must have gone to their brains.'

I thought briefly of the American lady with the nice voice and then quickly forgot her as the next medal presentation went ahead. The national anthem of Norway was played for the winner of the javelin.

A man sang along with the Norwegian national song and sounded like the Swedish chef from *The Muppets*. We laughed. The games were drawing to a close and, as I walked back to the floating palace, you could almost feel the melancholy in some of the spectators and volunteers.

'I reckon John Howard should get a gold medal for the work he's done,' said a nice-looking old nanna to her nice-looking daughter.

'No argument from me, Mum,' said her daughter.

People thought Howard was eminently sensible, a capable administrator and a super sports spectator par excellence.

But he seemed to need a minor miracle to win the approaching federal election in 2001. Around the country, successive state and territory administrations had fallen to the Labor Party. Ansett Airways, a major sponsor of the Australian cricket team and official airline of the Sydney Olympics, just disappeared one weekend never to return to the airports or the skies. Unemployment began to grow. Kim Beazley and the Labor Party did the sensible thing: nothing.

Almost a year after the Sydney Olympics opening ceremony, with its floating ships sailing through the sky celebrating Australia's connection to the sea, a trading vessel called the MV *Tampa*, manned by Norwegians and a captain with twenty-three years of experience, diverted from its course to the north of Australia to pick up survivors of a vessel taking water fast. The vessel was an unnamed boat trafficking in human beings, a people smuggler chock-full of people wanting to seek asylum in Australia.

The captain radioed for medical help and commandos from the Australian military inspected the refugees/illegal immigrants before providing medical assistance.

A controversy grew and distortion and accusation gave way to a breeding ground of suspicion.

An exclusion zone to protect Australia from infiltration by refugees/illegal immigrants was instituted.

I went to barbeques where people stood and drank their European beers and shook their heads and wondered where this country was going.

'I don't know anybody who voted for Howard. Not a single person. Where do these people all come from?' said a friend, swigging from a Peroni beer.

There wasn't much point reminding people that mandatory detention of illegal immigrants had begun under the Keating government. Why spoil a barbeque?

The longer the dispute went on, the more the Howard government's approval figures improved.

Some friends of mine formed a group called Actors for Refugees. They held a meeting in a gallery in Collins Street in the middle of Melbourne.

I was asked to read a piece about a group of refugees washed ashore on a Greek island. The locals walked down to the water's edge and provided the refugees with food, water and kindness. It was only a short little bit of text and I agreed to the reading.

Somewhere in the back of my brain I think I heard my father's voice, 'For Christ's sake, get involved, get up, have a go.'

On the appointed night I couldn't find the address and I walked up and down Collins Lane. Finally I found it. I pushed at the huge door, no give. There was no bell or intercom. I was running late. I humphed a bit. I was going out of my way to come help out after a hard day's work pretending to be someone very important.

I called out. I rang a number and got an answering machine. In the time-honoured method of rational human beings I swore and then kicked the door. It made a satisfactory boom. It sounded like the beginning of an old Rank movie, the kind that usually played on wet winter Sundays with people like Kenneth More and Dirk Bogarde in them, with the fellow with the short back and sides and oiled arms and chest banging the big gong with a hammer.

I kicked the door again.

'Come on,' I shouted.

I heard a noise and a small voice.

'Hello?'

'It's the police!' I yelled.

There was an intake of breath.

'No, no. It's William McInnes. I'm reading something. William... McInnes.'

'William McInnes?'

I thought of the heady days of the Olympics.

'Yes, I am locked out!' Well at least I made myself laugh.

The door opened. A face peered at me.

'We locked the door. We thought we might be interrupted... by the police.'

I could see she was serious. She even looked a little frightened.

I said sorry. She showed me down into the bottom floor of the gallery and there crammed to the brim was a vast collection of recognisable faces. It was a little like a social pages photo for the politically active. I looked around, nodded to a few people. I saw a host of Peroni activists, but of course they weren't. They were there because they wanted to be. I guessed a lot of them could never imagine anybody voting for Howard.

I thought of the nice nanna and her nice daughter. I thought of the suburbs of people twenty minutes from where we stood who would vote for Howard.

I read my bit of text. I read it okay until it came to the pronunciation of the nice humanitarian Greek island.

I did my best. But it wasn't good enough. I guess it always helps when you know exactly what is what. Someone in the crowd shouted out, 'That is not how you pronounce it. That is my home island. That is not how you say its name.'

I looked up.

'How do you say it?'

She said it.

I couldn't copy her. Inside I screamed, *Yes, I am locked out. What doesn't kill you . . .* I went on.

I got to the bit where the nice islanders helped the refugees.

The island's name was there. I paused, then decided to go without mentioning the island.

Her voice rang out. She said the name of the island. I wondered if she knew this piece.

I left the stage.

'If you couldn't say it, you could have asked,' she said.

A few people laughed.

I didn't think the point was about her island, or how it was pronounced. I thought it was about the people who were in sinking boats and being interned.

I never did another benefit. I never spoke again. I realised that perhaps to get up and have a go took a lot more than just turning up. It took the guts and commitment of my friends who would work nearly five years to make sure that their message was heard. But they weren't alone.

A couple of weeks later a journalist told me about Ian Chappell. How the former Australian cricket captain, the man Mr West had said was common, was speaking out against the treatment of refugees/illegal immigrants. Not in overt political terms, but just out of basic human concern. Out of common decency.

I told my mum about Ian Chappell as we sat in a marquee watching some poor bewildered, and probably underfed, American movie actor pose on some steps during Melbourne Cup day.

'Well that almost makes up for the safari suit. Very sporting of him,' she said.

'Oh I do wish they would leave the poor girl alone,' she added, looking toward the American actor.

My mum and I sat, drinking too much champagne and backing not enough winners. It was like being at the football. My mother, like my father and all of my family, loved yelling. Especially at people. She had already given an old pop star from the 1970s both barrels when he stood with his wind-tunnel face peering through a maze of cameras.

'You want your money back, mate!' she yelled.

But mostly she yelled at me. For I had started to grow a moustache for a role in a mini-series.

People would say hello and take in the sprinkling of hair on my upper lip.

They were too polite to say anything but thankfully my mother took care of things.

'I know! What does the boy look like?' She would boom. 'It's like he's got an anchovy on his lip!'

She was matched by the man who owned the television network that sponsored the tent we sat yelling in: the pleasant media magnate from the yacht.

'Jesus, Willy,' he said, looking at me. 'Don't tell me you've turned gay on us!'

My mother almost genuflected. 'Yes!' she boomed.

'I'm growing it for a job I'm doing at the ABC,' I said.

The pleasant media magnate considered me.

'Things can't be that bad, mate.'

I had no idea what he meant. I tried to help him by putting on my best charming actor voice. 'Do you mean the job at the ABC or the moe?'

The pleasant media magnate blinked. 'Both, mate...they're as bad as each other.'

'Yes!' screamed my mother. 'An anchovy!'

In the end my efforts came to no good end. My head was shaved and so was my moe, after the producer deemed it characterless.

I must admit that some part of me was a bit let down. Perhaps it was growing up in the seventies, the decade when hairy was cool, when every icon – from opening bowlers to movie stairs and tennis players, or even the fellow down the road who could do trick dives off the jetty – wore a moustache and other facial hair. I remembered GI Joe and his beard. I wasn't even up to his plastic standards.

We left the marquee when the Cup was about to start. The pleasant media magnate asked me and my anchovy where we were heading.

'Out on the flat, for goodness sake, where else would you want to be?' boomed my mother.

'Good for you,' laughed the magnate.

We made our way through the bedlam that was the flat at Flemington. All manner of costumes were on parade, not so much fascinators and race-day frocks but a bizarre fancy-dress pageant that reminded me of the kids dressed up for heroes day at the local school.

I looked around and saw lots of leery, beery out-of-its: a gorilla and a priest, and most amazingly of all, Don Bradman.

I knew he was Don Bradman because he had a badge above the make-believe Australian crest on his cap that said 'The Don'.

He stood swaying like he was trying to duck and weave Larwood's thunderbolts from the Bodyline series.

A nurse standing with him looked a little concerned.

'Are you all right?' she said. 'You okay?'

She actually sounded genuine.

'She's doing a good job,' my mother said as she posed for a photo with some Vikings.

'I'm not going to be sick… I'm not!' The Don said a little testily.

'You're shit-faced, Don,' said the gorilla.

'That's why you got a duck your last time out to bat, you lemon,' said the priest.

'You tell him, brother,' cheered on Mum.

'I…love Australia, greatest country in the world,' said The Don.

A pause and then everybody around us cheered.

The Don doffed his cap and, flushed with the success of his patriotic efforts, he assured his nurse he wasn't going to be sick.

'Oh, he's playing to the crowd all right,' said Mum and we waited for the national anthem to be sung.

One night in September 2001 in Washington, John Howard, dressed in his green and gold tracksuit, cheered on in front of a television as Lleyton Hewitt won the US Open tennis championship. Lleyton wasn't as blokey as Pat Rafter, and he didn't look like the sort of fellow you would readily sit down to have a beer with, but a grand slam was a grand slam.

John Howard laughed and applauded.

The next day the Twin Towers collapsed and the world seemed to be fuelled by fear and suspicion. John Howard fielded press questions in Washington and somehow managed to mention the *Tampa* illegal immigrants enough times to make sure that a connection was made by those who saw and reported.

His defence minister, Peter Reith, just filled in the dots: 'If you've got people moving in and out willy-nilly, then this can be a conduit for extreme terrorist groups.'

'Jesus,' said my brother Vaughan, 'he's taken sledging to a new low.'

'Look, people want to come here, they might just do anything to get here. Maybe they did throw their kiddies overboard, just to get saved and get here,' said a friend of Vaughan's as we drank in a pub. 'It's a good place to live, you know. Good place to raise a family.'

People wanted to hear more. Instead of weight-loss secrets and worst-ever holiday destinations, made-up talking heads spoke of terrorist cells and violent strikes against Australians in Australia.

The Howard government introduced a Border Protection Bill, but Kim Beazley's Labor Party wouldn't support it. Howard introduced it a second time and then Beazley passed it. He said it was a better bill. Howard said he had buckled to political pressure.

Kim Beazley said he didn't flip-flop.

But the whole idea of illegal immigrants as queue-jumpers struck a chord. A negative one to the Peroni activists, but a receptive one to many others.

People forgot about Ansett and rising unemployment. The new world order didn't care for localised issues. In a strange way, Howard became a big-picture player on a small canvas.

An election was to be held in November. But first there was a grand final to attend. On the 30th of September, just a few weeks after the awful events in New York, John Howard, my brother and myself, along with about ninety thousand other people went to Aussie Stadium to watch the National Rugby League's grand final between Parramatta and Newcastle.

The league was sponsored by a breakfast cereal that was designed to be eaten by super fit, super tough men of iron and its commando television ad was played over and over again.

This was despite the fact that earlier in the week senior players with six-figure salaries had wanted to pull out of an overseas tour with the Australian national team because of safety concerns.

'It's only a sport,' one of them said. It was funny. I thought it had become a business a long time ago. The players did very little else except train and play and prepare themselves, and yet all of a sudden it was only a sport.

Somebody forgot to tell the marketeers of the pre-game entertainment. A Seahawk naval helicopter prowled in low and revved its throttle, and then Jimmy Barnes appeared from its belly and started screeching 'Khe Sanh'.

Nobody seemed to waste much time thinking about it. Why should they? Enough dreadful efforts had been witnessed in the name of the pre-game warm-up. I wondered where all those wobbling June Dally-Watkins Pretty Women were. And what had ever become of the Roy Orbison impersonator?

But there was no irony. At worst it was just an old rocker earning a quid; at best people remembered Cold Chisel for a moment or two. Nobody seemed to make any connection to how military hardware and an anthem about a discredited war were being used to rev up a game of football. A game for which the players didn't want to travel overseas.

I thought of how people had laughed at the Norwegian national anthem. I had. But not tonight. Why laugh at the national song of the captain of the *Tampa*?

The election continued on its way and Kim Beazley tried to hold the line.

John Howard rallied his troops. He was never one to really give the full-throated call to arms. But this election he had his coach's line all worked out. The first time I heard it I couldn't quite believe he had said it.

'We will decide who comes to this country and the circumstances in which they come.'

People cheered. The Liberal Party used it in their advertising. I saw it, saw Howard and thought of the Swede, 'What doesn't kill you makes you stronger! Stronger! STRONGER!'

In the last two weeks of the campaign another vessel crammed to the brim with refugees/illegal immigrants moved through waters to our nation's north. It carried nearly one hundred and fifty children and over two hundred adults. Nobody knew the exact number. There was conjecture and there was theory, but nobody knew the facts. Except that it sank and nearly everyone perished with the boat. All those lives.

All those stories. All that potential. The possibility.

Who was to blame? That blanket will fall on no individual or individuals, for time moves on. Sometimes it is hard to find reason in life. Sometimes it is too hard to look.

We will decide who comes to this country and the circumstances in which they come.

The election came and went. The Howard government increased its majority and Kim Beazley resigned the Labor leadership.

The big cargo ships moved in and out past where I sat in the shot-put pit. The under-tens wound their way through, plopping the little shot as far as their skinny arms could throw. They were still so young, with so much to see and do.

I looked at my daughter. I looked at the ground teeming with tiny frames, moving the way butterflies do, with beautiful not quite fully formed limbs.

'It's for the kids,' the too jolly woman had said.

I looked up and saw the older man. He was telling a boy how to hold the shot tight to his chin and push straight out like his arm was reaching out. Pushing back the horizon. And I thought, what a phrase to give a child – pushing back the horizon.

The boy took the shot-put, stood still and suddenly, like a windmill, slung the shot-put up and down just near the old man's foot.

The little boy with baggy shorts jumped, yahooed and thrust his fingers out as if to signal a goal.

I laughed. The older man shook his head.

'Twelve years,' was all he said.

# 10

There wasn't a lot anybody could really say as we watched the television. We watched a man described as a Liberal powerbroker looking incredibly happy. Why wouldn't he? It had just been declared that John Howard and the Coalition had won control of both houses of government.

The man smiled.

One of the other people mutely watching broke the silence. 'Oh, I am sorry, I can't stand the way this smug bugger smirks. It's not even a smirk. It's worse than a smirk. It's a smurg. He's smurging.'

I looked at the Liberal powerbroker. He just looked happy. I had seen him look happy once before – on the top deck of the pleasant media magnate's hired yacht at the Sydney Olympics.

The powerbroker had sat by the pool with his awkward, chalky white legs in long socks, shorts and runners. He wore sunglasses that must have been truly expensive because they looked like they had come from a shoebox in an op shop.

He balanced a big plate of food on his thick knees. A woman floating in the pool called out to him, 'How are the chippies, babe?'

The Liberal powerbroker giggled. 'Fantastic! Yummo! The chippies have got chicken salt on them.'

'Naughty!' said the woman in the pool. She looked like she had crawled out of a vat of fake tan.

I didn't think it wise to tell anybody this when the Liberal powerbroker was, in the words of my friend, smurging away on the television, but it made me feel better. If chicken salt can't humanise a public figure, then what can? There have been times in my life when I too have jiggled in delight at the thought of chicken salt on my chippies. We may have been separated by our political leanings and bank balances, but we did share common ground.

'It's too much,' said my friend again, 'it's just awful. We're getting creamed...it's like watching us play Essendon.'

It was probably the most pertinent political comment of the night; certainly the most graphic. The Labor Party was just enduring another dreadful season in the Australian political game. A truly awful season.

The leader of the Labor Party, Mark Latham, appeared and conceded defeat. The silence in the room grew even heavier. The speech made John Hewson's 1993 concession speech look like a light-hearted and witty best man's address at a happy wedding reception.

'He looks likes he's been medicated,' somebody finally said, without a trace of humour or irony. 'The poor bastard.'

Nobody ever really thought that the Labor Party would win. Nobody I spoke to. But nobody thought the result would be such a shellacking.

As soon as Howard had said, moments after declaring the election, that the matter that most Australians would be considering during the coming weeks would be 'Who do you trust to keep interest rates low?', the election was over.

It wasn't as if anybody who had even a minor grasp of economics thought that a government could have any direct control over the level of interest rates in a free economy. Howard had never actually said that and there were always a lot of caveats and fine print as far as career politicians were concerned.

And the economy had certainly been running along quite nicely. The conservative parties in Australia always had a culture of management and they held the reins as well as anybody.

The landscape of Australia had changed. People's horizons seemed to stretch past their backyard, but only as far as their investment property or portfolio.

Neighbourhood services had changed from bakers, milkos and newspaper boys to wealth creators, financial planners and bankers who were available for meetings at any time.

Men with a steady gaze and friendly trust-me smiles would appear on television screens and guarantee that you would make money with them.

'Everybody thinks they're making money. People think they're getting ahead. They don't want to change,' my brother had said during the election. 'Labor is going to get creamed.'

A friend I had grown up with rang to tell me about an experience with a financial adviser.

'Jesus,' I said when my friend told me the financial adviser's name. 'Didn't he used to be a second rower for Redcliffe?'

My friend uh-hahed down the line. 'Yeah, but he's done a course.'

'What in?' I asked.

'I don't know, a financial planning course for second rowers.'

'What did he talk to you about?'

My friend said the second row financial planner had told him, 'It's all about hedge funds, mate. Hedge, hedge gives you the edge. You borrow against nothing to make a mint. Safe as houses.'

My friend had looked at him and said that if interest rates rose and the margins tightened then you could lose a lot of money as well as assets.

The second row financial adviser had looked at my friend.

'Know a bit about it then, do you, mate?'

My friend said he did.

'Nobody likes a smart-arse, pal,' was the second rower's opinion.

It wasn't just the cowboys though. Everybody wanted to be in on the new economy. Those Peroni activists had done all right out of the previous ten years. I had. Most had. Superannuation funds had swollen the share and property markets. How could we risk all this on an untried political leader who had a reputation as a loose cannon?

This had been played up for all it was worth in the election campaign: huge L-plates were hung around an image of Latham and scurrilous gossip about him was aired as hard news on some programmes.

Another factor in Latham's downfall may well have been my brother, Vaughan.

On many occasions during the election Vaughan had been stopped and mistaken for Latham. We all laughed a great deal and agreed that maybe if you squinted through one eye then, yes, he did bear a resemblance to the Labor leader.

Latham had been portrayed early in his term as a youthful and energetic leader. He had written about how the nationalistic and iconic captain Ian Chappell was amongst his favourite cricketers and he'd appeared on television at a social cricket match. Sadly Latham's man boobs became the talking point and, later in the year, pancreatitis laid him low in hospital.

Howard generously wished him well and walked more energetically than ever around the early morning streets.

So Latham's fragility became a questionable feature in his leadership.

This is where my brother came into play. My brother, like me, has a tendency to haunt drive-throughs and food halls filled with the golden glow of steaming bain-maries. He would sit and devour countless bits of produce that had been ordered through a microphone.

People would look at him and then stare.

'You should be looking after yourself, not eating this sort of dreadful food,' one old lady said. My brother nodded, gave a thumbs up and got on with eating.

When enthusiastically eating a hamburger in his car, a woman in a car next to my brother's yelled out, 'I knew there was a reason I wasn't going to vote for you... you disgusting pig!'

My brother nodded and gave the thumbs up again.

'Yes, Bill, I think I've torpedoed his food hall and drive-through vote. Could have been a deciding factor.' My brother had laughed a little and then said, 'People are too easy to scare. The threat of losing wealth they probably don't even have is powerful stuff. Latham's gone, but at least he went down gutsing himself!'

As Latham stared balefully through his sadly disconnected concession speech, there was nothing much for us to do except drink.

The next morning, earlier than I would have liked, I staggered into a municipal swimming pool brimming with screaming children and desperately excited parents. I had been dragooned into the role of timekeeper at a swimming carnival. Happily, for me and my head, I was sitting directly in front of the loudspeakers.

Every time an announcement was made I jumped and winced to such an extent that some of the times I recorded would have made Ian Thorpe proud. The two other timekeepers (one was extremely happy with the night before's result; she had been handing out how-to-vote cards for a Liberal candidate) took delight in my state.

Fortunately my services as back-up timekeeper were never required and the event ran as smoothly as these things can. It was a little anachronistic with the aged officials in their too-high trousers and porridge-filled sports shirts, their heads tilted as they stared intently at the kids splashing in the water.

But I noticed some of the competitors had things written in texta on their arms and legs: numbers and little phrases. A girl who barely looked ten had 'There is no tomorrow' written on one thigh and 'Who dares wins' on the other.

Child after child stepped up to the blocks with texta-covered legs. Glowering parents screamed from the bleachers.

'These kids...the words on them...' I said as I wrote down a time.

'Don't start me,' said the how-to-vote timekeeper. 'It's not their fault, it's not even the parents' fault. They just want to win. Don't start me.'

A girl took to the blocks. On her arm, in kiddie writing, was 'I am special, there is nobody like me in the world'. She glared at a girl in the next lane. They'd been the best swimmers of the morning.

They swam beautifully with steady strokes, gliding through the water. The girl in my lane came second, only a fraction after the winner in the next lane.

By the time she poked her head above the water she was in tears.

The other girl waited for the whistle to let the swimmers know it was time to leave the pool.

A parent ran to the side of the pool. The girl in my lane was still in tears.

'You swam beautifully, hard luck,' I said to the girl.

She ignored me.

'My turn, my turn, I slipped.' She sobbed.

The parent nodded.

'There are no tomorrows. No tomorrows,' the parent said and the pair walked away.

'Jesus,' I said. The emptiness of what some of the kids had written on their bodies was depressing. True, it was only some kids, but the fact that it was done at all made the weekend seem greyer still.

'Yes,' said the how-to-vote timekeeper. 'Aspiration or desperation, it's not very pretty. But what can you do?'

What can you do? That night I told my mother about the swimming carnival.

'Oh for Christ's sake, it's not the end of the world. All things pass. Look I bet you even money that old runty comes a cropper with both houses he's got. He won't be able to help himself.' She was speaking about John Howard. Yet she used the same term to describe him, Old Runty, that my father had given Bob Hawke.

The Labor Party stuck with Latham for a few more months and then he imploded completely. He seemed to have gone as soon as he had arrived.

'If you ever hear a cyclone named Latham,' said my mother, 'it's time to reach for the rosary, the bottle and bugger off. It'll be a town wrecker.'

But what can you do?

Well, you can broaden your mind. When I was little the star of the police show *Division Four*, Gerard Kennedy, made a fantastically creepy record of talking poetry. That's what my aunty Rita called it – talking poetry. It was her record so I guess she could call it whatever she wanted. Those days if you were popular in a television drama you would make a record. If you could sing, you'd sing. If you couldn't, you'd talk poetry.

So Gerard· talked. As I recall he whispered in a madman-like rasp, 'Travel broadens the mind.'

After Mark Latham's loss, I started Gerard Kennedying. Broadening the mind.

I spent five days in Hong Kong. What to do? Walk and watch. A big city with lots of people. Lots and lots. As I walked through the concrete and the glass I knew I was somewhere different, but also somewhere very familiar. Hong Kong is reassuringly similar to urban Australia. Big city. Big buildings. And even as I walked through the waves of Chinese faces I didn't feel like I was out of place.

I walked through the markets. Simon, the smiling concierge, had suggested I visit them to enjoy some local colour. There was plenty of colour.

In one stall, fish were dowsed in water and then placed on a plate to show how fresh they were. The fish's gills worked like a fan and the body arched, flipping on the plate. For a little encouragement the fish was dunked in some more water then placed out on the plate again. It flipped even higher.

I walked further.

Freshly cut meat hung from hooks and young butchers skilfully trimmed fat from deep red lumps of steak.

The next stall was a pet shop. Tiny, smug carp indolently swam around in safe circles as the carnage continued a stall away.

I reminded myself that it was a tourist market, and I remembered how much I'd liked the steamed fish dumplings I'd been served in a spankingly luxurious hotel overlooking the harbour.

I had sat high above the harbour in the breakfast area devouring the beautiful delicacies while two monotonous American businessmen went on in their great, flat clarion voices about timber prices and commodities, and how the French are so French and how China is the engine of the world for the next fifty years.

'Hard to believe how much China changes and how much it doesn't,' boomed one.

The other one stopped chewing and said very slowly, 'It's hard to believe that just over those hills, just over there, everything in the world is made. Everything.'

I stared out towards the hills. It looked cold. The cold makes you forget. I looked down at the yum cha and dim sum on the beautiful plates before me. Much better for me than the soft, microwaved chicken roll from the servo on Bondi Road.

I thought for a moment of the man who had served me there. He had gone back to mainland China. Big China. I wondered if he had found his nephew. Soon, he had said, all the old men would be gone. But they were still there.

It's funny how much China had changed, and how much it hadn't.

I picked up a dim sim and ate it. Lovely.

Suddenly there was a break in conversation and then I heard the flat clanging of the great, bearded American businessman.

'What is hard to believe is that Mel Gibson's been alive this long and he's only just now worked out there's a conspiracy,' he said in flat incredulity.

Oh yes, Gerard Kennedy was right, travel broadens the mind.

In the bar of the hotel I stayed in were lots of Australian expatriates. Accountants and lawyers who were loudly having a good time and enjoying being Australian. One matey and well-fed accountant sighed to me, 'I love Australia but it's just too small for me, too slow' and he drank his Boag's.

Travel broadens the mind, Gerard whispered.

'I do miss Sydney though, nice little town,' his friend, a happy and pleasant lawyer, said.

•

I looked out from a nice hotel room to the streets below. They were big and already crowded in the early morning. Sydney. It didn't look small or slow to me.

On the television, men with familiar faces, similar policies and bad suits banged on about Aussie Values. Immigrant tests and contractual obligations for Aussie Values. Aussie Values, it sounded like a meal deal you would order through a microphone. 'I'd like to upsize my Aussie Values for a large chips and hard work.'

Another grey face on the television, a political insider, informed me and anyone else who was watching that, 'It's a potential vote winner for the prime minister.'

Outside, I realised someone was calling my name as I jumped in a taxi. It was the director of a telemovie I was rehearsing. He trotted up to the taxi window and pointed at me with his finger.

'Don't let them cut your hair, William,' he said.

I gave him a thumbs up and the taxi took me to the airport. I was heading to the Kokoda Track.

Well, sort of. It was really Coolangatta.

I know back in the days of yore our troops had to survive the perils of wartime and submarines, but to get to Kokoda I had to survive the Indy Car Races.

They would test the nerves of any hardened veteran.

The only women on board were the flight attendants who wheeled the trolleys, and they were doing good business.

The plane was full of middle-aged race enthusiasts with merchandise already purchased, baseball caps with car brands already perched on their heads and drinks already doing the job in their innards.

By the time I got off the plane, my ears rang with the echoes of the Gavins and Dales and Todds and their plans for the Indy Races weekend.

The next morning I lined up at breakfast behind some polite Japanese tourists who looked anxiously at the rain falling outside the big glass windows of the dining area.

They looked as if they were dressed for golf and they carried their raincoats neatly under their arms.

They helped themselves to bacon, sausages, eggs and coffee. I had congee.

Then I waited outside with my not-to-be-cut hair, ready for my final trip to the Track.

The film was being shot on Mt Tamborine.

It's inland from the Gold Coast and when you climb up the high slopes there's a stark view of the abrupt Surfers Paradise skyline.

The last time I had been to Mt Tamborine was on a high school science excursion when a bad-breathed, and even more bad-tempered, teacher had tried to explain what the layers of rings on a tree trunk meant.

No one had really listened to him as the bellbirds called and his googly eyes searched for someone to answer his rhetorical question, 'Why is the history of this place important?'

I can't remember anyone answering him. I don't even think he offered his own answer. I can only remember his awful blue-striped jumper and his voice echoing in the rainforest. 'Well? Well? What's important?'

Mt Tamborine, now, seemed to be the home of some very pleasant houses. And the higher we drove the nicer they seemed to be. Houses were sprouting everywhere, like mushies after a thunderstorm.

It was raining and the clouds scudded low over the green hills. We turned down a muddy road and suddenly below us we saw the set. Kokoda.

The really great thing about arriving on a set sometimes is that it can take you to a different place and a different time. It's an impression, of course, because if you look clearly enough you can see through the work. But it's all about the moment. That day, due to a combination of the set designers' work, the rain, the greyness of the mist, the greenness of the rainforest and the abundance of mud, the set of 1940s Papua New Guinea was breathtaking.

I gingerly stepped through the mud, past returning soldiers gaunt with make-up and Papuan stretcher-bearers cradling injured diggers.

In the make-up van I saw an actor I was friendly with slumped in the make-up chair. He smiled and waved a tired hand.

'Have you read this script, William?'

'Don't need to, old mate... I know who won the war!'

There was a little bit of laughter and I thought briefly of the polite Japanese golfers at breakfast.

'Good you're doing the part,' said the actor.

'Yes. Yes, should be fun.'

The character I was going to be playing was based in part on Ralph Honner, a man I remembered my father speaking about with admiration and pride.

'A real cracker, that bloke. Would have done well in any man's army. A good man all right.'

My father had a lot of time for the men who fought on the

Kokoda Track. They were a part, he said, of an event that helped make modern Australia.

Australians who fought on the Kokoda Track didn't fight for the interests of rich and powerful friends or motherlands. They were fresh from the streets of our country and they were fighting for Australia.

And, during the course of this battle, something special happened, according to my old man.

Something that resonated on a generational level.

White, closeted Australian men saw, and were the beneficiaries of, the courage and comradeship of the Papuans. Black men who dressed and lived differently from those white Australians, but men with just as much courage and humanity as our own slouch-hatted diggers.

My father always regarded this as a step – a germination of a greater tolerance and understanding of the common bond of humanity between black and white.

'At least it made people think,' he said.

Playing the part of the captain was, in a minor way, like tipping my hat to my father's generation.

It was only a day's work and I'd decided to donate my fee to Legacy. So at least someone would get something out of it.

I sat in the make-up van. And sat and sat and sat. My hair that could not be cut seemed to be a bit of a problem. It wasn't that long, but it definitely wasn't your typical front-line Kokoda cut.

A hairpiece was suggested to thin my hair. It made me look like a rather sad customer of a Greg Matthews salon. Yeah, Yeah. No. No.

Finally, after hours of work, my hair was oiled, scraped up

and tied in a tight little bun. Then it was sprayed to a finish hard enough to crack a macadamia nut open.

I pulled on an infantry costume and wandered around with a shower cap to keep the rain off my nutcracker bun.

Somebody introduced me to an old man who lived below the mountain on the flats of Surfers.

He was with his wife. He would have been tall when he was younger, as tall as some of the made-up soldiers.

He was a veteran of the Track.

I sat and chatted with him.

And he said some of the most outrageous things about modern Australia.

'Not the country I fought for...we were white as cream buns in my day and we were British. Now we're a mob of bloody mixed all sorts, race of bloody mongrels. Oh well, I did my bit. It's up to you folk now.'

I felt embarrassed about play-acting a war. Why wouldn't a man of that generation hold some of the prejudice and belief, or simple longing, for that time?

It's not as if they could have foreseen what Australia would become. No more than the Anzacs when they fought at Gallipoli. Did they fight for a secular, multiracial society? No, they fought in the name of a country that has become a different world.

There is a lot of guff spoken about mateship and its sacredness to being Australian.

Mateship is used to sell almost anything. I flew up with a planeload of men who were probably enjoying being amongst the mateship industry at the races, drinking and carrying on.

But the old man I spoke to had actually lived it.

An assistant director came and told me it was time to travel down to the set.

As I walked off, the old man said, 'You know one of the stupid bloody things about today? Every silly bloody football or hopscotch or social club has to go off and walk the Track.'

'The Kokoda Track?' I asked him.

He nodded.

'It's as if they have to go there to prove something. If that makes it more real! By Christ, what's wrong with reading a bloody book about it? Get on with living your lives here! Make this place work. Silly sods.'

The Australia that old man had fought for had changed. Changed into a big, rich, multi-layered society.

I replaced my shower cap with a metal helmet. I was ready to address the troops.

I slipped and slid in the mud.

Why make the film? Why? Why tell the story?

Like that goggle-eyed teacher of mine had shouted to the rainforest, 'History is important.'

And at least I knew one thing – I hadn't let them cut my hair.

Sometime after the Kokoda Track experience I saw a newspaper photo of Kevin Rudd smiling with an old fellow in a pub and drinking a beer. I knew very little about Rudd. But I knew there was something interesting about the photo.

I looked at it again. He was dressed like he had been hiking. I read the text. Rudd was having a beer with some old codger in a pub in North Queensland and he was sharing a laugh about his experiences on the Kokoda Track, which he had just walked.

I told myself to remember Kevin Rudd.

The bank manager sitting in front of me seemed nice enough. I looked around her office. There was a series of inspirational posters. A man running up what looked like the steep seating rake of an empty sporting stadium. 'Effort makes us different from the next man.' These were the kinds of things that were texta-ed on the little kids at the swimming carnival.

I asked the manager what she thought of Kevin Rudd. More to break the silence than for any other reason.

She didn't look up; she was studying something on a document. But she kept repeating his name over and over. 'Kevin Rudd, Kevin Rudd, Kevin Rudd... I don't know... but I think he... is...'

I hung on her words.

'...is... pretty sensible.'

She looked at me and smiled.

'And...'

She paused again.

'I like the way he walked the Kokoda Trail.'

I thought it was funny the way older people called it a track and most people now called it a trail.

'My husband did it with his footy club. Really good to touch history. Good Rudd did it. I don't know about him, but that impressed me.'

I nodded. I looked at another poster over by the air-conditioner. Edmund Hillary on top of Mt Everest.

'Why? Because it's there' was written on top of the poster.

I stared at the image of Hillary and remembered a night in Rockhampton.

I must be the only person to sign a life insurance renewal and have in my mind's eye a giant spiralling turd with match-sticks stuck on the top of it.

'Because it's there.' I laughed a little too much.

The manager looked at me.

'Just thinking of Kevin Rudd and the Kokoda Trail,' I said, struggling to come up with something.

She looked at me.

'Pretty...good...he did it. I couldn't,' I said lamely.

She stared at me with a steady gaze. 'It's amazing what you can do when you put your mind to it.' I thought that she was going to suggest I write this on my arms in texta.

I initialled again and scuttled away from the office.


It was good to be part of a crowd. Exciting. Something was in the air.

So many people were swarming like ants towards the stadium for a night at the cricket. Young couples, families, lots of mums and harried, eager-looking fathers with baseball caps and backpacks, and kids with faces painted green and gold. Australian flags furled and unfurled, waving about in excited little hands.

'Hey, watch what you're doing! You'll have someone's eye out!' came the timeless and all-purpose fatherly warning.

Lots of loud banter weaved around the statues of Miller and Ponsford and Lillee. Lines of orderly, enthusiastic Australians going off to watch the nation's premier sporting team in action.

It was like an illustration from an Australian Values calendar. A celebration of sport with orderly enthusiasm.

Especially if you compared it with the 'disgraceful scenes' at the Australian Open when Serbian and Croatian tennis fans exchanged racial insults and were ejected from the Rod Laver arena. You wouldn't find that on the Aussie Values calendar.

A hundred and fifty people were ejected from the Open for causing a disturbance. Racial taunts between the two groups were thrown this way and that.

I feel uneasy when I see flags draped across the backs of angry and aggressive young men, see their fingers pointed and hear them yelling racial taunts. It's a reminder of the divisiveness that exists in the world, of the old hatreds that split communities.

'There's no place in Australian sport for that sort of racially driven animosity,' said newly appointed Opposition Leader Kevin Rudd. And good for him. No argument there.

But as well as the happy, painted faces and young families at the cricket there were other Australians. Like the group of young men with bulging bags of beer walking in front of me and my son, swerving off underneath Keith Miller's statue and into the dark car park to devour the full-strength beer before presumably topping themselves up with the mid-strength beer available at the ground.

Oh well, I told myself, they're just having a bit of fun.

It's easy to shrug your shoulders at such behaviour. I like to have the odd beer myself while watching the cricket.

Lots of spectators had snuck in beach balls and there were great roars of approval as the balls bounced around, away from the grasp of ground officials. Just a bit of fun.

Later in the night, after the boorish Mexican wave had showered people in the lower stands with rubbish, half-eaten takeaway food and the odd tennis ball, a new inflated item appeared in the crowd.

A blow-up female sex doll.

The doll was bounced from group to group.

'Oh they're giving her some,' said a man nearby who was dressed in a variety of brand names.

I looked at the doll. At how the crowd were 'giving her some'. Young men, quite a few of them full as ticks, were thumping and kicking and pounding 'her' into the air. Her legs were wrenched this way and that. A glass of mid-strength beer was poured down her open mouth.

I felt uncomfortable, even ashamed. Of blokes.

It was as if every woman and little girl had been pushed to one side and told, 'You don't belong.'

I looked at my son and his mate. I wished they hadn't seen the doll and the way it was treated. I was glad my daughter and my wife hadn't.

But just because they didn't see it, didn't mean that message didn't exist. *You don't belong.*

The doll was taken away by security and skewered with a knife, but almost to prove a point another inflatable instantly appeared.

'Look, a big finger,' a young boy cried.

There, bouncing around in place of the doll, was a huge inflated penis. It wasn't thumped as much – some of the young blokes posed with it and then rather nervously flicked it away. But it wasn't long before the huge 'finger' was thrust and waved around like some mad collective boast of masculinity.

I could almost hear those father's words again. 'Watch what you're doing, you'll have someone's eye out.'

Soon after there was a fight in the upper tiers of that stand. The last course in a night of inanity. A fight that turned attention away from the skills of the players we were there to watch.

One hundred and fifty people were ejected from the tennis. None were arrested. There were arrests at the cricket.

Idiots and bores come in all shapes, sizes, colours and religious denominations. A drunken lout at the cricket, a loudmouthed nationalist at the tennis. One person's idea of disgraceful behaviour is another's idea of a bit of fun.

For there are a number of Australias.


Caboolture used to be a farming and dairy area. Now it is a place of signs. Billboards, sprawling prefabricated shopping barns and housing estates. It has also been earmarked as the site for a potential nuclear power station.

As I drove through, an old woman on a scooter, festooned in maroon and white streamers, beeped the tiny horn at people in her way. Leaning on a palm tree nearby, a man in an old Queensland Rugby League jersey chatted and laughed with his shadow.

'The hometown of Keith Urban,' said another sign.

To think they want to put a nuclear power plant there.

'It's Origin Week', said yet another sign, just in case anybody had forgotten.

The next morning Origin jumpers, hats and flags were everywhere.

I accompanied my mother to her Tai Chi class, run by a man called Kevin. An elderly woman in her late seventies, wearing a Queensland State of Origin jumper, unfurled her

Flying Goose. She looked at me. 'I'm a proud Queenslander,' she said. And she is. For she is my mother.

In Origin week Queensland is pushed into identifying itself through its relationship with New South Wales, or more pointedly, Sydney. And it's all one way. Sydney is the centre of evil. 'Those Mexicans in Sydney! They'll cook the ref! Maroon wash!' screamed the headlines. Huge photos of huge men with huge jaws and bored eyes stared at me from newspapers and televisions.

The whole mad, silly thing was fun.

Only in Queensland, where the home state had already won the series, could everybody walk around and still feel like the underdogs.

On game night I sat in a local footy club with one of my oldest friends. We had watched the very first State of Origin in 1980 at Lang Park. A different time. The sport wasn't professional then and all the players had a trade or profession to ply during the week days. Now most players are professional athletes, trained and tapered to perform their 'sport'.

Next to us a man frantically answered a phone call from somebody at home. He tried to explain to the person on the other end how to turn the television on.

'Press AV... or TV... Press it again... anything?'

A groan from every crevice of the club was heard when former New South Wales coach Phil Gould's massive head appeared on screen.

'You busted arse.'

'Press... press DVD.'

'Oh Christ,' my friend muttered. He pointed to a man with a tight haircut, bushy black moe and a watch that looked like a silver brick on his wrist. It was the financial planning second rower. He was standing at the bar, laughing with some colleagues. We heard him say, 'Yeah well nobody like a smart-arse, pal.'

Willie Mason was booed and heckled. 'You happy hand-clapper! Let go of his head.'

Young men downed alcoholic soft drinks. The man next to me was still whispering instructions.

'AV, press AV...it's there...it must be there.'

A lone New South Wales supporter cheered a little too loudly when Queensland's Brent Tate was injured.

'You cat!' he screamed.

'Come on, turn it up,' I heard myself yell.

The young New South Wales supporter turned and yelled, 'I used to play this game and I'm naturalised.'

What that meant was anyone's guess.

As soon as the game started, it was over. And Queensland lost. Lost. An announcement was made over the club intercom, 'Attention patrons, the result of tonight's Origin: Queensland 4, the Referee 18.'

There was a few minutes silence and then a pleasant and bewildering calm descended. Testosterone disappeared into the ether.

A man two tables away with maroon war paint on his middle-aged cheeks and wearing an ill-fitting Queensland jersey, took off his Toad Warrior headband and turned to his friend.

'I'm just going to fetch a chamomile tea, like one?'

Not long after the game, I shared a cup of tea with my mother.

'Kevin Rudd, Mum. What do you think of him?'

'He's all right...he's a Queenslander.'

I laughed.

'Well, you know, the only good thing that ever came out of Nambour until now was the Big Pineapple.' She lifted her eyes upwards and shrugged. 'We'll see how he goes.' And she patted her dog and sipped her tea.

The 2007 federal election seemed to stretch from the time Kevin Rudd took over from Kim Beazley in December 2006 to election day. It was a long grinding process with a series of polls and constant analytical bombardment by experts who basically banged on about the same thing.

It was like listening to the expert commentary on a sporting broadcast, because all that was said was the obvious and, in most cases, to quote my father: 'The only reason the experts are experts is because they have a bloody microphone shoved near their cake-hole.'

The longer the campaign went on, the more people got used to the idea of life without Howard. He had been around so long that he was almost like a long-running soap opera villain or hero. But he was just another man. It's often forgotten that when his wife was seriously ill in his first term he thought about giving the whole kit and caboodle away. During the election though, the prevailing attitude about Howard was more in line with what John Hewson had said of Howard's attitude to being prime minister, 'You'll carry John Howard out in a box.'

I saw Howard once at, of all things, the launch of a ship. He had turned up at a shipyard in Williamstown to launch a frigate. I had always liked going to see big things when I was a kid and they don't come much bigger than the launch of a ship. Ship launches only seemed to happen in black-and-white documentaries on the History Channel. And who better to officiate at a black-and-white documentary than John Howard?

The Williamstown docks were strewn with flags and bunting, and a brass band played beneath blue skies.

For some reason, whether by chance or design, the band decided that an appropriate tune to play when the prime minister turned up was *The Pink Panther* theme. I laughed. When I was a boy a hospital had opened up the road and there had been bunting, blue skies and a band that had played *The Pink Panther* theme. There had also been a fat tough in a judo-cum-karate outfit who was going to break some pavers. I had once seen this man demonstrate a 'bushman's hanky' at the Redcliffe showgrounds. A bushman's hanky is when you hold one finger over one nostril and clear the other nostril with a great blast of air. The bushman's hanky.

Sadly for the fat tough he bushman-hankied over half his body shirt.

He was, by Mum's terms, 'Not quite right', so when he attempted to break the pavers with a massive martial arts scream, *The Pink Panther* tune seemed quite appropriate.

He'd brought his arm down with a scream and brought it back up with a yelp. Then he staggered around with, 'Fuck me sideways, I fink I broken me arm.' Amazingly he got a round of applause.

So did the prime minister as he got out of his car and waved to people. His two minders were soon caught up in the crowd. I lifted my daughter on top of my shoulders so she could get a better look. As I did I wondered where on earth people like the fat tough go. Well, I didn't think he was here watching the prime minister of our nation make an entrance to Inspector

Clouseau's theme song. It was all slightly odd but, in a strange way, reassuring.

Howard was surrounded by a group of people, kids mostly, and he waved as he slowly made his way through them.

'Oh hello! Hello there! Hello!' He sounded like somebody doing an impersonation of John Howard. He seemed to be enjoying himself. One of his minders stood only a few paces away, shaking his head.

I pointed to Howard and asked my daughter, 'That man there, that man, do you know who he is?'

A week before we had been in Ballarat and I had wanted to see the city's Avenue of Prime Ministers, a row of sculptures of Australian PMs lined either side of a path in the city's gardens.

We had pointed out various names to match the faces and then, sensibly, I had attempted to leapfrog over as many leaders of our nation as I could.

Don't ask me why, I don't know.

What I do know is that after leaping Bob Hawke and Keating me and my wherewithal came unstuck on John Howard and I found myself clinging and grimacing on the PM's bust.

This event had obviously impressed my daughter.

'That man is the prime minister, that's John Howard,' I said.

My daughter looked at him and said, 'That man there, you sat on his face. That man there.'

Howard's minder was close enough to hear and he looked at me and, without a smile, said, 'Well, mate, you are keen. Whatever gets you through.'

•

There wasn't much to get John Howard through that election. 'Who do you trust to keep interest rates low?' had been his bumper-sticker slogan in the last titanic election. Every time I had seen it I'd thought of the stickers football teams hand out at the beginning of each new season.

This time Kevin Rudd's bumper sticker seemed to be the one that people remembered. 'Working Families.'

That was it. Working families. Every time Rudd opened his mouth he mentioned it, even in his sleep.

The election ground on and on. Howard with his storming of shopping malls and his early morning stalking of suburban streets, and Kevin Rudd looking like the Thunderbird who was sent to university instead of going into the family rescue business, and sounding a little like Ned Flanders from *The Simpsons*.

My mother explained it was simply because he was, 'Bright, very bright, but he comes from Nambour so, you know dear, there has to be a bit of a pay-off.'

She wanted him to win of course. 'He's a Queenslander for Christ's sake – who else would I vote for?'

On the day of the 2007 federal election I took my son to his school cricket match.

I watched him and his team-mates. What they were doing at that particular moment was all that really mattered to them. I thought what a wonderful thing it was to be in the moment.

I lay down and listened to them call for a quick run and then say no, and then say yes, and then say sorry. I heard them laugh and call each other by their nicknames. I thought what a good thing it is for children to be allowed to be children for as long they can.

It was a beautiful day. I remembered how my father had loved elections, even ones he knew he or his chosen party wouldn't win. The day could have been as miserable as a scrape of boarding house butter, but he'd always clap his hands and roar, 'By Christ, it's a fine day for the vote!' And he'd be gone, handing out how-to-vote cards and doing his election day stuff.

I didn't hand out how-to-vote cards, but I did work the sausage sizzle stand at the local primary school and the rest of the afternoon went by easily enough. Democracy with a sausage, fried onions and tomato sauce.

An old man from around the corner came whistling up to the sausage sizzle.

'How are you travelling, brother?' he sang out.

'Pretty good,' I said. I asked him with a wink who he was voting for.

He feigned amazement.

'Whoa! Come on, comrade – the only thing I am slightly ginger about is the name situation. I mean John and Peter. Kevin and Wayne. I'm plumping to get rid of an apostle and a disciple and replace them with Kevin and Wayne from the bloody Sunshine Coast!' He laughed and took a fat sausage to keep him company in the booth.

We went to an election night party. The feeling in the room was no different from a grand final barbeque.

A debate broke out about which television broadcast to watch. Finally it was decided that we would surf the network coverage.

'But I don't want to miss Antony Green!' shouted somebody.

Some other people cried out his name.

'Antony! Antony!' It sounded like a *Countdown* audience screaming out for 'Woody! Woooodeeee!' from The Bay City Rollers.

One television network had decided that democracy wasn't as entertaining as it could be and had turned the whole event into a sideshow. I felt the hand of Hale and Hearty at the helm.

The panels looked like the old *Wide World of Sport* and *Sports Scene*: half-hearted vaudeville efforts with silly competitions like pie-eating, woodchopping and weightlifting, and people competing for a pack of Hutton Footy Franks, a Dandy Ham, a sports bag by Addy-das, some Tang – 'The stuff they drunk on the moon, you know!' – and some sports rub.

All it needed was a handball competition or a Commonwealth Bank pass-the-ball hole, where a footy player would toss the ball through a smiling elephant target. If the pass was successful it would release a blast from an air horn and the host would slyly say, 'Well done, son, you've made jumbo a happy boy!'

Peter Costello appeared on the screen from his electorate celebrations. It was pretty clear that the government was going to fall. He was only about six or seven years older than me and he had spent nearly twelve years as treasurer of this country. Twelve years. On the television that night, he looked much more relaxed and comfortable with himself.

I had once stood in line for a coffee in a suburban coffee shop. It was a nice shop, lots of families and lots of neighbourhood chat. A man at the front was laughing and gently teasing his daughter. She elbowed him back and he laughed even more. His daughter giggled and then hugged him.

They turned with their coffees and there was Peter Costello. It was a bit of a shock to see him in such an environment.

He looked like a pleasant enough man who enjoyed mucking around with his family. Twelve years he had spent in government, twelve years where he had probably only snatched little bits of family time. No wonder he looked relaxed now.

When it became clear that Kevin Rudd was going to be taking home the Dandy Ham and Tang, I decided to head off to the Trades Hall in the city with a couple of friends while some others went to burn an effigy of John Howard in a backyard.

Maybe that would seem a bit more like an election night. A bit more about democracy. But maybe the vaudeville act on the television was a part of what we had become. What we all expected.

Trades Hall in Melbourne is a grand Victorian hall with imposing columns and massive staircases. A heavy building that reeks of history. From outside it looked forlorn and empty.

We entered a side door and walked past a crowded ballroom where people stood toe to toe watching a huge screen. We went down a staircase to the basement where an even bigger screen was set up.

Food was being sold, beer was being poured and people were dancing. It didn't look like any election night party I had ever seen. It was more like the Collingwood victory in 1990. Only this time there was no point post to climb.

The cry went around that Howard was about to concede.

'I want to see him cry!' screamed somebody behind me. 'I want to see him in tears!'

Howard, of course, was Howard. He was booed like the captain of a losing team in a grand final is booed. And when people couldn't boo any more they heard a speech that was right out of 'How to Make a Graceful Concession Speech 101'.

'He didn't cry! I wanted him to cry!'

As if on cue a man wearing a huge John Howard papier-mâché head came dancing out, followed by some women dressed up as 1950s housewives. They held a bat of some sort and swung it at the Howard head. It fell. They hit it more. They hit it as often as they could. But the head just seemed to take all the blows without any obvious impact. Soon the head was rolled away, presumably to some dark corner where musty artefacts are kept.

Then Rudd was introduced on the big screen by the Queensland Premier.

'A great Queenslander,' I heard her say.

I screamed at the top of my lungs and roared with laughter. 'QUEENSLANDER!'

Where was Artie Beetson?

Rudd got up and smiled and spoke and spoke. And *spoke*. The crowd in Trades Hall lapped it up.

He thanked our great friends the United States of America. There was a roar and then a bit of puzzlement.

I don't know what else was expected of him, what the crowd wanted. He thanked all the working families that had voted for Labor, perhaps for the first time, and he said the government would earn their support.

A few people stared at the screen.

A friend of mine turned to me. 'Mate, this fella is going to break a lot of these people's hearts.'

Another man who heard my friend's remarks turned to us. 'Mate, that's bullshit. I may be naive – but I got hope. I think this fella is something.'

'Oh Terry, you're just drunk, you're not naive,' said a woman who was with him.

Terry looked at her and shrugged his shoulders. 'What's the difference?'

We left soon after. This time we walked up the big stone steps out to the front of the Trades Hall. The steps were immense. They reeked of time. I looked down as my legs started to a hurt a little. The steps were worn in the middle. You don't see that much in Australia. That evidence of history. Of human movement, of lives having worn their mark in hard stone.

All those footsteps, all the people who had struggled and lived and dreamed.

I suddenly understood that perhaps it is right to have hope, to be naive. To believe. It is right to struggle, to live.

I walked a bit further, the steps turned a corner and I stopped dead.

A huge picture, as big as a wall, stood before us.

I stared at it for some time. Its size was quite startling but it was the image that held me.

It was a massive print of Gough Whitlam.

An image I had not seen before. He looked handsome. Grand. But it wasn't the supercilious Gough of those election posters from so long ago. He looked away from the camera, his fingers gently cupping his chin and mouth. He seemed pensive. Thoughtful. It was such a humble shot of him. It was as if he contemplated the briefness of time. The transitory nature of power.

I thought suddenly of Open Sesame. Of what he seemed to be trying to say that day I waited for the big Mercedes to pick me up to take me away on my Saturday. Of how Whitlam smirked above me on the placard outside my parents' house. A lifetime ago. A thousand lifetimes. Where are you now, Open Sesame?

He probably wasn't trying to say anything.

I remembered the words of the old drover. 'We're all just passing through.'

I looked down at the marks worn in the steps.

'Night, night, Gough,' I said and I walked up and away from him.

# Epilogue

Not so long ago I spent an afternoon in Old Parliament House in Canberra. Even though Canberra is one of those towns that many people love to roll their eyes at, I came away feeling uplifted.

As I wandered through I thought of the schoolgirl I had loved. I wondered where she was now, and if she still liked beef sandwiches.

I drifted about looking at the portraits of the prime ministers and overheard a tour group's efforts to understand our history.

'Can you tell me who this might be?' asked a guide, pausing by a bust of Harold Holt.

'Sir Donald Bradman,' came a voice from a little group of people old enough to have voted for Holt.

'No, not The Don,' said the guide. 'Although it might have been interesting on the Chinese sub if it had been him.'

Billy McMahon looked almost sensible in his bronze form – the sculptor had worked a minor miracle. Menzies looked suitably wise and owlish. John Gorton looked as if he was more interested in what was happening outside the frame of his portrait. Paul Keating was elegant in a grey suit but his pale hands were clasped in a childlike way and he appeared slightly embarrassed and surprisingly devoid of a chin.

Mal Fraser's portrait showed him with his trousers hitched high. 'A real choko Charlie,' as my father would have said.

As high as they were hitched they still ended up around his ankles in Memphis, and there has to be a metaphor about a fall from power there we can all appreciate.

I thought of my father a great deal as I walked about. He adored elections and politicians. He loved a fight and a debate. He would often say that parliament was 'the people's church'. 'Never take democracy for granted,' he'd say, 'never. Too many good people died giving it to you.' And then he would invariably add, 'And never vote for a bastard with a beard. They're hiding something.'

Well, obviously the founding fathers were up to something for they nearly all had beards to a man, save for Edmund Barton.

I listened to some old video footage on loops and what amazed me was the almost frightening articulate gifts of Whitlam.

'He's a bugger who could talk underwater,' my lifelong Labor voting father once said. 'And for the life of me I can hardly bloody keep up with the man.'

It was as if he was from another planet.

I stood behind a couple who gazed up at Andrew Fisher in his morning coat. After a long while the woman said to her companion, 'Another Queenslander.'

'Hmmm,' the man intoned. And then, 'His hair is the same colour as Rudd's.'

The woman nodded. 'Queenslanders,' she said.

Around the pillar was the man one of those Queenslanders had replaced.

'Oh dear, look at him,' said the woman as we all looked at John and Janette Howard. She said it with the tone one uses on seeing some poor, half-silly cousin at a large family Christmas.

The Howards were dressed as if they were going to such a reunion and this provoked a shaking of the woman's head.

'Trust him. Everyone else is formal and he has to go neat casual. It's like they're off to a buffet.'

'Well, you voted for him.'

'I don't care. Neat casual is inappropriate.'

Eleven and a half years as PM and your era is deemed Inappropriate Neat Casual. And that's by people who voted for you.

I walked off and stood on the steps where Whitlam had said his famous words in 1975. Tea towels are sold showing Whitlam bubble-speaking those words. History on a tea towel.

I looked down at the Aboriginal Tent Embassy. The War Memorial loomed in the distance. I thought of all the names engraved there.

I realised the view hadn't changed from the first time I'd seen it.

'Never take democracy for granted, too many good people died to give it to you,' my father's voice said.

I heard some footsteps behind me. It was the man and woman who had been looking at the paintings in King's Hall.

'We should still be in time for Beryl's do if we hurry,' said the man.

'Well just be careful you don't fall down Gough's Steps,' said the woman.

The man turned to say something and tripped slightly. The woman laughed.

He didn't fall but he did that thing men do when they stumble a little in the street. They stop and inspect the area in the cement where some shoddy piece of workmanship has undone them.

The woman laughed. 'There's nothing there, you just tripped up because you were rushing.'

'That'd be right,' said the man, 'you'd know.'

They walked off to their car.

I looked after them and then I sat down. On Gough's Steps. We all trip up some time. We all stumble a bit. As long as we keep going.

Australia isn't perfect, it doesn't have to be for it is the sum total of its people. We are all good and bad, eager and indifferent. Some of us don't care, some care too much, most of us go about our lives. That's it.

'Yeah,' I said to myself, 'that'd be right.'

# Acknowledgments

I would like to thank the following, in no particular order of importance. Sarah Watt, Clem McInnes, Stella McInnes, William West, Barbara Masel, Deonie Fiford, Vanessa Radnidge, Rick McCosker, Bernadette 'Batman' Foley, Kate Taperell, Louise Sherwin-Stark, Amy Hurrell and all at Hachette Australia.

Thank you.

# Also available

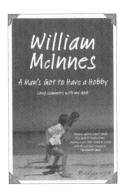

*'Life goes by so fast that sometimes it is good to wait and let the memories catch up. And there is no better place to do that than the backyard where you grew up.'*

*A Man's Got to Have a Hobby* is a look back at the life of Colin McInnes, father of five, handyman and habitual Stubbie wearer, and his wife, Iris, lover of shopping centre openings, Volkswagens, and Dean Martin. It is a story about cane toads and backyard barbeques, French–Canadian Hell Drivers and footy games. Through the memories of their second son, William, we are transported to a time when incinerators took up space in every yard and K-Tel glass cutters were the pride of many a home.

This is a book about people who aren't famous...but should be. It is about love and hope and fear, laughter, death and life.

'William McInnes compels with the sheer delightfulness of his memoir, and with his fine ability to spin a damn funny yarn.'
Lucy Clark, *Sunday Telegraph*

Cricket Kings
William McInnes

Chris Andersen loves cricket. He may not be a legend like Bradman or Boonie, but in the Yarraville West Fourths, Chris Andersen is king. He is the captain, the coach, the manager and, thankfully, a player. They are getting hard to find...players.

Every Saturday in summer Chris ropes together a motley team of men and a couple of boys to turn up in their cricket whites to try to win a game. Everyone has a different reason for being there: to hear the music from a nearby house, to block out the memories of another place, to entertain themselves, to please their dad, or just to have a go.

And everyone has a story to tell.

'A book about a lot more than cricket... And even though you laugh out loud, you recognise something real.'
*The Age*

'A unique piece of work that brings alive a suburb and a game that are both part of the national psyche'
*Sydney Morning Herald*